W D Lumgair.
From cherryl + Paulla

Silver Linings

Silver Linings

Stories by
GREGORY CLARK
Pictures by
JAMES FRISE

The
CHARACTER
METER
SHOWS THE
STRENGTH
OF YOUR
CHARACTER
AT A GLANCE

COLLINS • TORONTO • 1978

Silver Linings
by Gregory Clark
Pictures by James Frise
Selected and Introduced by M. J. Worek

This selection first published 1978
by Collins Publishers
100 Lesmill Road, Don Mills, Ontario.

©1978, the Estate of Gregory Clark and
the Estate of James Frise

The stories and pictures in this volume
were first published in the *Star Weekly*.

Canadian Cataloguing in Publication Data

Clark, Gregory, 1892-1977.

   Silver linings

Selections taken from stories appearing in the
Star weekly, 1934-1935.

ISBN 0-00-216699-2

I. Frise, James, 1891-1948. II. Star weekly.
III. Title.

PS8505.L32A6 1978   C818'.5'208   C78-001522-3
PR9199.3.C52A6 1978

Printed in Canada

Also by
Gregory Clark
and James Frise:
THE BEST of
GREG CLARK
and JIMMIE FRISE

The Stories

Introduction

I last saw Greg Clark in 1970 when I asked him, as the acknowledged Canadian authority, to help select material for a series of books about the outdoors. He was living at the King Edward Hotel in Toronto and, although I did not realize it then, was still very much like the drawings of him done by Jimmie Frise forty years before.

Eight years later, I came to know a younger Greg Clark while reading the hundreds of stories he wrote in collaboration with Jimmie Frise. The stories in this book were meant to add a leavening of optimism and fun to the heavy load of gloomy news that the old *Star Weekly*, along with the other papers, had to carry during the Depression years of the 1930's. Greg and Jimmie were an instant success and helped us weather one of the most trying times in our history.

If I could have only one story to read again, it would be "Strength of Character", originally published in January 1934. This story has everything that made the whole series famous. Greg and Jimmie decide that there should be more to life than the nine to five routine. They need to return to the independent spirit of the pioneers. To prove they can do without modern conveniences, they start to walk home from work, but end up taking the streetcar when it gets too cold. Then they try to cook their food over an open fire, but end up ruining the meal and filling the house with smoke. Finally, they run out the backdoor rather than face Jimmie's wife when she sees the mess they've made.

The point of the story, as true today as in the middle of the Depression, is that people measure themselves by the things they have the courage to attempt rather than the things at which they succeed. No matter what the result of any action, it pales in relation to the hopes that even the most humble of us have for it, in our dreams.

Greg Clark showed millions of depression-weary Canadians that there was still a silver lining inside those clouds. Here, at least, in the weekly Greg and Jimmie story, Canadians who knew they were worth more than the times allowed them to show, could enjoy themselves amongst friends.

The stories in this book are the best of those written during 1934 and 1935. Enjoy them, that is why they were written in the first place, and why they reach across 40 years to give us so much pleasure today.

M.J.W.

Silver Linings

Strength of Character

January 20, 1934

*It was a wonderful pioneering
feeling that filled our bosoms.*

"You're not," said Jimmie Frise, "the man your great-grandfather was."

"I suppose not," I admitted. "Did you know him?"

"What I mean," said Jim, "is that to get along at all in your great-grandfather's time you had to be strong. Nowadays anybody can get along."

13

"In a way," I said.

"Every year," went on Jim, "it becomes easier for the weak to compete with the strong."

"So much the better," I stated.

"Oh, I don't know about that," said Jim. "Just hold on a minute. Where you get out of bed in the morning, in a house heated with a furnace, your great-grand-father . . ."

"Call him Ebenezer," I put in.

"Ebenezer had to creep out of bed in an ice-cold shanty and light a fire in the stone fireplace. Where you get your breakfast on a gas stove, Ebenezer had to cook his at the open hearth. Where you back your car out or catch a street car, Ebenezer had to walk to his job."

"I don't think the winters were as cold in those days," I said. "At any rate, not being accustomed to steam heat, they wouldn't feel the cold the way we do."

"In your great-grandfather's time," continued Jimmie, "it was easy to pick a man of strong character. They stood out over the heads of all the men of weak character. Men of weak character succumbed to all the hardships of climate and toil. Nowadays it is as easy for a man of weak character to get along in life as it is for a man of strong character."

"The weak still fail," I argued.

"Yes, but the whole scheme of modern life is to prevent them failing," said Jim. "It won't be necessary much longer to have strong characters."

"Holy doodle, Jim!" I gasped, as the power of his argument lifted me.

"Your great-grandfather Ebenezer," went on Jim, "wanted a wife. Having demonstrated his strong character by the way he stood the hardship, stuck to his job, delivered the goods, he was entitled to one of the best girls in the neighborhood. And he got her. To-day a girl doesn't have to be much of a hand to be a competent housewife, with ready cooked foods, newspapers full of menus and ideas, electric devices for cooking and cleaning. How much variety would a modern girl get into her cooking if she had nothing but an open fireplace to cook on and if she had to walk three miles to the nearest store for her groceries?"

14

"How much variety did Ebenezer's wife get?" I inquired.

"We're All Getting Soft"

"Men can make a good living nowadays," said Jim, "just sitting and watching a machine. In the olden days there used to be a sort of fat, loquacious man who sat all day on a barrel in the corner store, discussing everything. To-day that fat man is a big shot salesman, with the help of a car to haul him around from barrel to barrel all over the land."

"Life is certainly filled with opportunity these days," I admitted.

"But no opportunity to demonstrate character," said Jim. "And that is why leaders are so hard to find, all over the world. Only a hundred years ago our leaders stood out clearly defined in every village. And they chose our leaders for the country. And the leaders of the countries directed the world, with firm hands. No doubt they were often wrong. But they were firm. It is that firm touch we miss to-day."

"What are we going to do about it?" I asked.

"We could give up our motor cars and walk to work," said Jim.

"My great-grandfather never walked eight miles to work," I said. "And even if he did, it wasn't across a hundred streets filled with dangerous traffic. It was along pleasant paths through the woods."

"We ought to do something," said Jimmie, uneasily. "I feel as if we were all getting soft. This is the era of ease and comfort. When it is so easy to keep warm, get good food and earn an easy living, why should we bother about vague, faraway things such as Ottawa or Geneva or Hollywood or the chain broadcasting corporations? They are our real rulers. But why worry?"

"We could take out our telephones," I suggested, "and send our kids over to do the messages to the stores."

"That would be good for our kids," admitted Jim. "But it wouldn't strengthen our characters."

"I feel all weak inside, Jimmie," I said. "I never realized how soft my character has become."

15

"Look at the Scotch," said Jim. "They are noted all over the world, in business, politics, war, for their strong character. And it comes from the fact that they have no fancy modern inventions in Scotland."

"Do you suggest we stop all inventing and bust up all the factories and wreck Niagara?" I cried.

"Which would you rather have?" retorted Jimmie, sternly, "comfort or character?"

"Well, we've got comfort," I said. "Can't we get character, too?"

"How?" demanded Jimmie.

"We could all start thinking about it," I ventured.

Resolving To Go Primitive

"You can't add one cubicle to your character," declared Jimmie, "by taking thought."

"Well, then?"

"Well, then, this very night," cried Jimmie, "we will go primitive! We will try to recapture some of the stern stuff our forefathers were made of. We will test ourselves, just to see how far we have fallen, how shabby our strength of character is, our resolution, our firmness. We will start by walking home from work!"

"Oh, Jimmie, it's a cold night!"

"My ancestors," shouted Jim, "trekked forty miles through the virgin winter wilderness to carry a sick woman to the nearest doctor!"

"My great-grandfather Ebenezer," I claimed, "drove a heard of twenty cattle from Holland Landing to the town of York for twenty-five cents!"

"We'll walk home to-night," declared Jim.

"What will our wives say?"

"My wife is out," said Jimmie, "for supper and for the whole evening."

"I'll telephone my wife and tell her I have to work to-night," I said.

So we started at five-thirty to walk to Lambton, where we live, near the banks of the Humber.

It was a fine cold night. Our spirits were inspired by the feeling of character actually growing within us. We set out, as Jimmie explained, to follow the old Dundas road which Colonel Denison cut through the wilderness during the War of 1812, to allow travellers to escape the American gunboats lying off the mouth of the Humber which would shoot at wayfarers following the lake shore highway.

Side by side we strode out Dundas street and we passed the Grange and Spadina avenue and were well past Bathurst street before we began to slow up a bit.

"How do you feel?" asked Jim.

"My character feels a hundred per cent improved," I replied, "but my feet are starting to hurt. Our ancestors didn't have to wear shoes like ours and walk on hard icy pavements. They wore moccasins and walked on lovely, soft snow."

"The more your feet hurt, the better for your character," said Jim.

"It seems a long way to Roncesvalles," I said. "And then from there to the Humber . . .!"

So we took it a little easier and talked about other means we might discover for improving our characters.

"One thing we will do," said Jimmie, "when we get home, we'll go to my place and cook our supper on the open fire over the grate! My folks are all out to-night. We can have the place to ourselves."

"Ham and eggs," I said. "Boiled potatoes."

"And tea," said Jim. "We'll boil the potatoes and the tea and fry ham and eggs. That's the sort of food our ancestors cooked on the hearth."

"Is it a wood fire?" I asked.

"No, I've nothing but soft coal, but we will get some wood on the way home."

"How?"

"If we pass a wood yard," said Jim, "we could each carry an armful. Or maybe we could go down in the valley by the Humber and cut some wood. That would be better. There weren't any wood yards in our great-grandfathers' days."

These discussions spurred our feet, but by the time we got to Lansdowne avenue, to what used to be called the White Bridges, I noticed even Jimmie was picking his feet up tenderly, while I had sharp aches up both my legs and my feet were sore, as if scalded. But my character was shining inside of me like a 60-watt bulb.

"It's ten minutes past seven," said Jim. "Perhaps this is enough character building for to-night. To get on with the cooking before my folks get home, perhaps we had better take the street car."

So from Lansdowne we took the car, and walked from the end of the bus line to Jimmie's house. We got an axe and went down to the end of the street and into the Humber ravine.

"We want pine and birch," said Jimmie.

"It is illegal to cut trees down here," I warned him.

"Men of character do not let technicalities deter them," said Jim.

But no matter how woodsy the Humber valley looks in summer you would be surprised how few fire-wood trees there are. We slithered and slid around the valley for nearly half an hour before we found a birch tree and a small fallen pine. And while I kept watch for the county police Jim cut firewood. And with two good big armfuls we climbed the hill and hastened back to Jim's without meeting any police and hardly any surprised pedestrians.

In no time we had a splendid fire roaring in the grate and it was a toss-up which shed the brightest glow about Jimmie's living room: our characters or the crackling wood fire. Jim got a couple of fancy candles from the dining room and lit the living room with them, turning out the electric lights.

He got two pots and the frying pan. I peeled the potatoes while Jim arranged some pokers and curtain rods on the fire basket to serve as cranes and hobs, such as our ancestors used for cooking.

On the living room table Jim spread bread and butter, salt and a Spanish onion.

Wonderful Pioneer Feeling

There glowing with the loveliest glow, we squatted before the fireplace and started to prepare our meal. We set the potato pot and the tea pail on the rods and got the frying pan hot for the ham and eggs. Owing to the fact that Jim's fireplace was not originally intended for cooking, the addition of these pots and pans in some way affected the draught, so that a lot of smoke got into the room.

"But that is all the more real," said Jimmie. "Our ancestors lived in smoky rooms."

The potatoes took a long time to start to simmer, and there was no sign of boiling in the tea pail, when Jimmie, in moving the frying pan, tipped the potato pot over and the water put the fire out.

It took all of fifteen minutes to recover the potatoes and get the fire going again.

"I guess you had better go down and cut some more wood," said Jim.

19

"It's against the law, Jimmie," I said. "We got away with it once. But the law of averages is against us. This time, we would be caught."

"There isn't enough wood left," said Jim.

"Seeing this is our first experiment," I said, "let us fall back on coal. Our ancestors were resourceful men. They would not have hesitated to use coal if it were handy."

So we put soft coal on and had a splendid fire in no time, though it took the potatoes a terrible time to get started again. Once they did start to boil, it took one man all his time lifting them off every time they boiled over for fear they would put the fire out again.

With the tea pail and the potatoes boiling merrily, and the ham and eggs sizzling in the pan, I tell you it was a wonderful pioneer feeling that filled our bosoms crouching there in our shirt sleeves before the open fire. It was now nine-thirty, and we were hungry enough to eat a horse.

The coal cracked and spluttered a good deal, and quite a lot of black smoke got into the ham and eggs. They caught fire once, and Jimmie leaped back so violently with the frying pan ablaze that he upset the potatoes again. But there was so little water in them that it did no harm.

"Now," cried Jimmie, ladling the ham and eggs onto plates on the table. "Now how does your character feel?"

"I certainly have an empty feeling," I said, "if that is character."

Jim laid the frying pan down, and there was a hiss as it scorched a big bubbly ring in the living room table top.

"Not so good," said Jim, laying the pan back on the brick hearth.

When Character is Rugged

The potatoes were not quite boiled. The ham and eggs tasted of coal. The tea tasted of something funny, but we never discovered what it was. But character, when it is strong, can stand for almost anything in the way of food. We were just finishing our meal when Jimmie cried: "Hist!"

There were sounds on the veranda.

"Quick!" cried Jimmie, leaping up. He led me out through the kitchen, the back porch and into the dark yard.

"No time!" he gasped. "My family!"

"But where do we go?"

"We'll hide out here for a while, until they get over it," said Jimmie. "And then we will go back in and say we know nothing about it."

"It's an awful mess," I said. "Those pails and pans and the wet wood ashes, and smoke all through the house, and that burn on the table!"

"We'll say we were at a movie. We'll say it must have been burglars that broke in," said Jimmie.

"But our coats and hats are inside," I protested.

"We'll say we just ran out for the police."

"Jimmy!" I cried. "Is this character? Lying out of it like this?"

"They would never understand," said Jimmie.

"We could explain that we were building up our characters, we could tell them the whole story," I said.

"No, I have a better idea," said Jim. "Let's go over to your house and I can stay there until my folks are all in bed, then I can sneak in. It is easier to explain things in the morning than at night."

So in our shirt sleeves, we hustled through the night to my house. It was easy to explain our shirt sleeves to my family, because we told them we had run out suddenly from Jimmie's to see a car crash we had heard in the night, and it was half way to our house, and we just ran over here to let Jimmie see a new book I had on dogs.

Jim and I sat drowsily in my den until about one o'clock and then, he wearing one of my old coats, I let Jimmie out quietly.

"Good luck," I whispered.

"I'll be all right," replied Jim.

"Sneak in softly," I warned.

"Leave it to me," said Jim softly.

So, full of character, we parted.

On the Mend

February 3, 1934

"Can you run over, for a minute?" asked Jimmie Frise on the telephone.

"I've just settled down," I said, "for the night, with a good fishing book."

"Well, I've got a poor chap here, I wanted you to see him," said Jimmie. "It's a pathetic case."

"A friend?" I asked.

"No, he just came to the door," said Jimmie, in a guarded voice. "He is selling necktie racks. A very nice article. But he lacks salesmanship. He hasn't got the punch. And he broke down on my porch. Run over for a minute, will you?"

"Surprise," I said. "Madame, here is a
surprise for your husband. This tie rack . . ."

23

"I'm no good in cases like that, Jimmie," I demurred. "I always break down, too."

"Come on," begged Jim, "we'll go into a committee on him."

So I threw on my coat and walked over to Jimmie's.

Jim had him in his little study at the side of the house. He was a man in his thirties, not badly dressed, but with that drawn look of despair and defeat on his face that is familiar to any of us that answer our front doors. Beside him on the floor was a paper bundle containing about a dozen objects made of wood with numerous pegs sticking out of them. They were painted pink, or blue or white.

"This gentleman," said Jimmie, when I walked in, "makes these tie racks himself."

I examined one critically.

"It's a very attractive article," I said with a professional air.

"But," said Jimmie, "this gentleman can't sell them. He simply can't sell them. He has gone from door to door all through this well-to-do neighborhood and he hasn't sold one!"

"I guess I'm not cut out for a salesman," muttered the tie rack man huskily.

"Wasn't anybody interested?" I inquired, sitting down sympathetically.

"Most of them just opened the door, and before I could say a word, when they saw me hold out the tie rack, they shut the door," said the man. His mouth was working, and tears stood in his eyes.

"It isn't," said Jim, hastily, "as if these were some commonplace junk. These are an original conception. Made by hand. Designed to fill a long-felt want in almost every home."

A Surprise Selling Line

"Yes, sir," said the man, sniffing loudly, "I thought them up myself. And I made the first model myself. And I perfected it myself. And I produced them in quantity myself. Painted and all."

"Well," I said, "nowadays you have to have a selling idea as good as the idea in itself. It's no longer true that the world will beat a pathway to the door of a man who makes a better mouse trap. Nowadays, the only pathway beaten to any mouse trap manufacturer's is to the one who advertises and has worked up a smart selling line. In fact, the only pathways at all are those beaten by tireless salesmen driven by a tireless sales manager. Today, the best mouse traps in the world aren't catching any mice, if the inventor is simply sitting at home looking out across the lawn for a path to appear."

"You mean," said Jim, "that this gentleman ought to get some manufacturer to adopt his idea?"

"Not if this gentleman wants to make any money out of it," I replied. "I was merely suggesting that we think up some smart idea for him. This is old territory he is working. Every door in this neighborhood has been opened ten times a day for the past three years by somebody with something to sell, useful or otherwise. He has got to have some way of keeping that door open for half a minute, for even fifteen seconds, until he sinks the harpoon of interest into his prospective customer."

"That's true," admitted Jim. "Now what would you suggest?"

"For one thing," I said, "I'd have a couple of nice snappy ties hanging in one of these racks when I hold it up as the door opens."

"Great!" exclaimed Jimmie.

The other poor chap sat up with interest.

"Then I would say something like this," I said, getting up and holding one of the tie racks in my hand, as if I were at a door. " 'Surprise madam, a surprise for your husband. This tie rack hanging handy to his dresser, with all his ties neatly and tidily displayed. Only fifty cents. It will keep his dresser tidy. It will tend to make him interested in his appearance. Only fifty cents. In three colors. To match your furnishings!' "

I sat down amidst applause.

The man was impressed and flushed.

"Gents," he said, "I sure am grateful. I'm sure I can do it. You've put new life into me. But I don't think I'll try to-night. I'll wait till to-morrow. I'm all in to-night."

"No, no," cried Jimmie. "Try it to-night. While the

25

idea is fresh upon you. Why, you can get rid of this dozen to-night in half an hour."

"I'd rather tackle it tomorrow when I'm fresh," said he.

Making a Poor Start

"Think of going home to-night with six bucks in your pocket," said Jimmie, earnestly. "I believe in striking when the iron is hot."

"Gents, if you don't mind," said the poor fellow anxiously.

"Listen," cried Jim. "I know how you feel, this salesman stuff is terrible at first when you aren't used to it. I tell you what we'll do. We'll go with you for the first few calls and get you started."

"Would you!" exclaimed the tie rack man joyfully. "Would you?"

"Sure," I said.

"We certainly would," said Jim. "We're interested in human nature experiments like this."

Jim dashed out for his coat and hat and the man picked up his bundle of tie racks.

We went out, taking Jim's car.

"We'll drive a little way," said Jim, "just to get away from this immediate neighborhood where we're known."

We drove up a couple of blocks and parked in a comfortable neighborhood and began at the first house in the block.

"Now you be the salesman," said Jimmie "and we'll come right with you, carrying the stock of merchandise."

We rang the bell. I cleared my throat.

A lady came to the door.

"Surprise," I said, bowing slightly and employing a regular salesman smile. "Madam, here is a surprise for your husband. This tie rack hanging handy to your husband's dresser . . ."

The lady, who had been looking with astonishment from one to the other of us, slowly closed the door. She didn't even say scat.

In silence we walked down the steps.

"There you are, gents!" said the tie rack man. "That's it!"

"One swallow doesn't make a summer," said Jimmie. "The bad beginning means a good end."

Nobody was home but the young folks at the next house, they were dancing to the radio and the seven or eight of them who answered the door didn't have fifty cents.

The next house, only the maid was in.

The next one, only the man of the house was in, and he had the book he was reading in his hand, and you could see his mind was not on what we were saying.

"Surprise," I cried, holding the tie rack up in front of him. "Sir, a surprise for yourself! This handsome tie rack hanging handy to your dresser with all your ties neatly and tidily arrayed . . ."

"What the heck!" he said suddenly. And as suddenly slammed the door.

We went back out to the pavement.

The tie rack man was getting impatient. You could tell by the way he kept silent and stared off down the dark street moodily.

"Think of a new line," said Jim. "Try some other approach."

Trying the Heart Appeal

"How about this?" I exclaimed. "All three of us stand in the doorway, each one of us holding out a tie rack, you the blue one, you the pink one, and me the white one. What you call mass appeal. And then I will say: 'Madam, these are tie racks. They are a useful and ornamental object for every man's room.' "

"No good," said Jimmie, "we would only frighten the woman."

"I guess you gents had better let me get along," said the tie rack man in a melancholy voice.

"No, sir, once we put our hand to the plow!" cried Jimmie.

"Look here," I cut in, "why not employ the one appeal that has worked to-night? What got this man into your

27

house and brought us out into a committee of the whole? Why, the heart appeal!"

"Tears," cried Jimmie.

"The breakdown," I said. "We will call at this next house and we will all three stand there with tears in our eyes, and appeal to the lady to buy a tie rack, we haven't sold one to-night!"

"And that would be true," added the tie rack man.

"Don't overdo it," warned Jimmie.

We went up to the next house. We turned up our coat collars and stood in an abject huddle while we waited for the bell to be answered.

A bald-headed man in shirt sleeves came to the door.

"Mister," I said, exhibiting the poor pink tie rack, "us three have been all over this neighborhood trying to dispose of these tie racks, we only ask fifty cents, they're a lovely thing, handy as anything, and we made them ourselves (here I let a little quaver get into my voice) and painted them ourselves, our own idea, too, and we thought we could make an honest dollar or two out of them . . ."

The bald-headed man stood looking at us silently. The tie rack man was the picture of woe. Jim had his chin ducked down in his collar, his hat over his eyes, a look of desperation in his attitude.

"You haven't sold one, eh?"

"No, sir," I said, brokenly. Jim gave what sounded like a miffled sob. The tie rack man lifted his wan face into the light.

"By george," said the bald-headed man, "step inside here a minute!"

Generous With Advice

He held the door wide, and we three trooped into the hall. Beyond, there was a table, through a haze of cigar smoke, at which sat three men playing poker.

"Just a minute, boys," called the bald-headed man. "Step out here."

The poker players got up and came into the hall.

"These three poor chaps," said the bald-headed man, "have a very handy little article here, a tie rack. See? A

28

handy little gadget. They made them themselves. They thought up the idea themselves. They painted them. They have been all over this district and haven't sold one! Now, here's a case where we ought to help, don't you think?"

All four of them regarded us with deep sympathy.

We all sat down in the front room.

"You fellows look like pretty respectable men," said the baldhead.

"Yes, sir," I said. "We're all good honest mechanics, and we thought we could make a few honest dollars to help along. But it seems we can't sell these things."

One of the men opened the bundle of tie racks and they all passed them around, admiring them.

"A smart idea," they said. "A first-rate article. A thing you would imagine would sell in any house."

"Yes, sir," I said. "Any man would appreciate having a thing like that to keep his ties in order."

"Sure," said one of the poker players, "my ties are all hanging on a knob by the mirror on my dresser. All in a mess."

"I tell you what," said the bald-headed man, "you fellows have got a good article here, but no matter how good your article you have got to have a selling talk to go with it. It isn't enough just to show them at the door from house to house."

"That's true, sir," I said. And Jimmie nodded brightly.

"Now, we four men," said the bald-headed man, looking around at his three friends who were regarding us sympathetically and curiously, "are in the merchandising business. In fact, this gentleman is something of a wizard at selling. I think we could get together right now and give you a sales talk on these articles which would work magic. You could dispose of this lot in no time, the three of you."

"You're right, Bill," said the others, nodding.

"Now, let's see," said the bald-headed man. "How about this: you walk up to the door and when the lady comes you are holding the tie rack up like this, see? And you say, right off: 'Madame, the problem of keeping your husband's ties in order is one of the banes . . . no, not one of the banes . . .' "

"The problem of keeping your husband's ties in order," stated one of the other poker players, a tall, thin, thoughtful man, whose tie was all skew-gee, "is promptly solved by this simple, attractive and handsome little article, only fifty cents."

"That's better," cried the bald-headed man. "Or how about this: 'Madame, how often do you have to sort out your husband's ties, all in a tangle in his bureau drawer? This handly little article, etcetera, etcetera.' Do you see?"

The New Message

Jimmie and the tie rack man and I all saw, but the tie rack man had a slight bulge in his eyes that I did not like.

"I tell you what we'll do, boys!" cried the bald-headed man. "We'll go with you! This is most interesting to us, as sales experts. We're not in the mood for cards to-night anyway, are we, boys? No. So just wait a jiffy and we'll step out with you and see those racks vanish with a little snappy sales approach."

"Good idea," agreed the others, rising.

"Won't there be a lot of us calling from door to door, sir?" I asked respectfully.

"I was going to suggest," said the tall thoughtful man, "that we might each take two racks apiece and we will scatter along the block and make a game of it. See who disposes of his racks first. Eh, boys! And so select the best sales talk."

His friends all snapped up the challenge.

"How about it?" asked the bald-headed one, genially. "Will you trust us?"

"Oh, yes, sir," I assured him, nudging the tie rack man, who seemed to be on the point of saying something.

We trooped out the front door.

"You chaps work right along here," said the bald-headed one, "but as we others are known around here, we'll walk a couple of blocks north and start. When

you're through wait here, will you? We'll be back in no
time!"

We divided up the package of tie racks, giving each of
the four gentlemen two apiece. Pinks and blues.

They walked eagerly away and Jim and the tie rack
man and I started down to the corner of the block for
Jim's car.

"Now for a getaway," I exclaimed.

"Where do I get off in this?" demanded the tie rack
man loudly.

"Ssssh!" said Jim. "We'll pay you for the lot. Three
bucks each, me and my little friend. Am I right?"

"Right," I said, opening the car door and hastening my
two companions into it.

"But where do you get off in this?" asked the poor tie
rack fellow, bewildered.

"It's worth three bucks each to us," I explained as Jim
drove quietly but smartly away from there, "for the lesson."

"Lesson?" said the tie rack man.

"Sympathy and advice aren't enough," I said. "We are
all learning that now. Those four guys right now are
learning it, too! It's the new message of good times returning."

"Yes," said Jim, "we'll buy your stuff even if we don't
need it."

"And even," I added, "if we haven't got it!"

"Well sir," said the tie rack man, "I do believe things
are on the mend!"

Paint Job!

March 10, 1934

"Your car," said Jimmie Frise, "needs a paint job."

"It has reached the stage," I admitted, "where it either has to have a paint job or it has to be turned in."

"With an engine like that," said Jim, "you would be crazy to turn it in."

"The funny part of it is," I said, "a paint job at the moment seems more expensive than the first instalment on a new car."

"Heavens!" said Jim.

"A paint job," I pointed out, "will cost $50. Right now. Whereas the first instalment on a new car will only come to about $38. And then I won't have to pay it till a month from now!"

Jimmie looked at me curiously.

"I suppose," he said, "the bulk of the public is like you."

"I pride myself," I agreed, "that I am an average man."

"I tell you what," said Jim. "I'm an artist. Color is my line. I am free and easy with a paint brush. If you like I will help you do a paint job on your car."

"A home-made paint job," I demurred, "always looks amateurish."

*Rusty saw a cat. Then the tragedy happened. He chased
the silly cat . . . it took a flying jump on to the car . . .*

"Sir," said Jim, indignantly, "not even the most expert car painting establishments have artists in their employ!"

"I beg your pardon, Jimmie," I cried hastily. "Of course I would be delighted to have you help paint the car. The only fear I have is that I might undo all the good you are capable of doing. I am a terrible painter. I get paint in my hair. Inside my shoes. It is incredible."

"With me to guide you," said Jim, "I think you would do a very good job of painting."

"After all," I agreed, "if we make a mess of it, I can turn the car in."

"Now how about the color?" asked Jimmie.

"It is a kind of beige now," I said. "A lightish brownish color."

"Isn't it funny," said Jim, "how many bright-colored cars are shown at the motor shows and how many drab black, blue and other dull-colored cars the public buys?"

"I was thinking," I said, "of a nice dark blue. It would be a nice change from its present color. And if we do a good job, the neighbors might even think it was a new car I had."

"Funny," remarked Jim, "how many new cars the neighbors sell!"

"Say dark blue with black fenders," I suggested.

"I see," said Jim, "that at heart you are a chartered accountant! You have a cold, mathematical mind! For you there is no joy in life. You have no soul for color."

"I love color!" I cried. "I know no man who goes as crazy as I do in the spring, at the sight of tulips, daffodils . . ."

"Yet you want a black car," said Jimmie. "You want to add to the gloom of this sad city. Toronto, with its sober streets, its drab windows, its cautiously dressed people. Never a splash of color, never a joyous burst of bright hue."

"Express Yourself in Color"

"It is in the air of this country to be sober," I pointed out.

"What!" shouted Jim. "With Ontario and her blue

34

skies, her intense greens, her world-famous riot of autumn reds, purples, golds and yellows! With half her surface water, Ontario is one of the most colorful lands in all the world!"

"M'mm," said I.

"As a true Canadian, a true denizen of Ontario," went on Jimmie, excitedly, "you ought to express yourself in color. You should rebel against drabness. You, a son of the fifth and sixth generation in this glorious, color spangled Ontario!"

"Quite so," I admitted proudly.

"And here you have the chance of a life-time," said Jimmie. "You are going to paint your own car, with the help of an artist. Let your car bespeak your true Canadian character!"

"What color do you suggest?" I inquired.

"Colors!" cried Jim. "Not color. I suggest a red body for the red leaves of October. Blue mudguards for the blue sky of Ontario, and the blue water of our myriad lakes. And the top . . ."

"Black," I said.

"Everybody has a black top," cried Jim scornfully. "Why not use a little imagination? I say, paint the top like an awning, which, after all, a top really is. Paint it red and yellow!"

"Oh, Jim!"

"Yes, sir, red and yellow, for the autumn leaves, for the fruitful grain fields of Ontario, for the yellow sands of Wasaga Beach and the shores of Lake Ontario and Lake Erie!"

"Jimmie," I breathed, "you are inspired!"

"How about Saturday afternoon?" demanded Jimmie, hotly.

"Done!" I said. "Let's see, I'll buy the paint. Red, blue, yellow."

"And better get a little green for trimming," said Jim.

Saturday noon, I had the garage laid out with all the paint and the brushes, step-ladders and so forth. My family was away for the day. Jim arrived the minute he was through his lunch and we donned our overalls.

Jim took a bed slat and ruled off the roof of the car into stripes, as we did the top first so as to have any paint drip down on the lower works before they were done.

"Now," said Jim, "you do the yellow stripes and I'll do the red."

From the top of stepladders it was no trick at all to do stripes.

In the winter sunlight that top looked lovely.

"I am sorry," I said, as we surveyed it, "so few people will be able to see it."

Unfinished Symphony

Then we started on the tonneau. Rapidly the scarred beige of the old car vanished under the proud, bold strokes of two patriots laying on the red of autumn leaves, the red of wintergreen berries, the red of wild strawberries, of Indian flame, of the scarlet tanager and the red-headed woodpecker, and all those other beautiful things we have in Ontario.

"We're spilling a lot," I said to Jim.

"The blue will cover it," cried Jim, who was quite carried away by his emotions. He was swinging his paint brush the way the conductor of a symphony orchestra swings his baton during those rich, juicy bits.

Rusty, Jim's so-called Irish water spaniel, was sitting watching us with delight. Next to water, which he has hardly ever seen, Rusty loves paint. He is an artist's water spaniel and has chewed up many a tube of water colors in his day.

We finished the red, and started on the blue. The chassis, they call it. The blue was the blue of Ontario's sky, of her lakes, of the eyes of her fairest daughters. I tried some out on one side of the hood.

"We should do this to music," cried Jimmie, "we should have the radio playing 'O Canada.'"

"Jim," I said doubtfully, "take a look at it now we've done this side."

"A symphony!" exclaimed Jim.

36

"It looks like an advertisement for something," I said. "Gum or maybe barber's supplies."

"It is an advertisement," cried Jim. "An advertisement of Ontario, of her boundless color, of the spirit that animates at least one citizen of this joyous, flaming country!"

"But will my mother-in-law go to church in it?" I said. "If any of my folks get married, can we go to the wedding in it? Or won't I run up the price of an ordinary paint job in taxi bills?"

Jim gave me a cold, long stare.

"Have you no imagination?" he asked.

Jim was up on one mudguard and I was over on the stepladder at the far side, sopping up some pools of yellow and red that had gathered in the corners of the roof, when the tragedy happened.

Rusty saw a cat. He chased the silly cat. The cat ran around the car a couple of times, and then took a flying jump on to the hood.

"Arrrgh!" screamed Jim.

But I was glad.

The cat slithered over the hood. Rusty followed, with swimming motions. The cat leaped to the roof. I helped it.

Rusty skated all over the roof. Onto the hood again and along the mudguards.

Then up the alley they chased. So I went around to Jimmie's side where he was shading his artist's eyes with his cleanest hand.

"Let us call this the first coat," I suggested gently, "and as soon as this dries, give it a good coat of black all over."

Jim peeked at it through his fingers.

"Marbled," he muttered. "Or shot, like silk. A sort of modernistic effect."

"Or what do you say I turn it in?" I asked.

"I believe in signs and omens," said Jim. "I guess this means to turn it in."

So any day now a car dealer is going to get a shock.

Upsadaisy

April 7, 1934

He lifted and tossed me brutally into the air so that I fell on the hard cold pavement.

"Let's strike!" said Jimmie Frise.

"Strike what?" I inquired.

"Let's strike against the working condition of the masses," went on Jim, "or something!"

"What's the matter," I asked, "feeling kind of beany to-day?"

"No," said Jim. "Full of sympathy. I am just brimming over with the desire to help. To improve. To aid, I would like to march in forbidden parades and attend illegal assemblies."

"You would be recognized," I said, "as one of the comfortable middle-class and the strikers would have nothing to do with you. One of them would bonk you with a chair leg."

"I have often wished," went on Jim, "that I had been a garment worker or a mill hand instead of an artist. When you are an artist, you have nothing to live for. No principles to starve and die for. No fellow-workers to stand with behind the barricades. I can't imagine a bunch of artists holding an illegal assembly. Even in Toronto."

"You're well off the way you are," I remarked.

"The way you talk," said Jim, "you would think life consisted of eating and sleeping. Have you no soul? Don't you ever long for life to be dangerous? Don't you sometimes dream of having ideals that you could declare, of beliefs that you could fight for? What do you get out of life, just eating three meals a day and sitting down to a typewriter every so often?"

"Life," I replied, "consists of being comfortable and doing a good day's work . . ."

"Who for?" demanded Jim, darkly.

"For myself," I said. "Making a nice living, putting something by for my old age."

"You might just as well never have lived at all!" cried Jim. "The world is filled with people like you, just plodding dully through life, content to be young, then middle aged, then old; stupidly working away, day after day, year after year, and whether they ever lived or not makes no difference either to the world or to themselves."

"You would prefer, I suppose," I asked, "to be back in the prehistoric ages when there were only a few scattered tribes of men on earth, and every day mattered so much to them that they either lived or died that day!"

"I certainly would!" cried Jim. "We are the descendants of those wandering tribes. We inherit their countless ages of action and warfare against the elements, fierce beasts, enemy tribes."

"I bet they longed for peace and comfort," I put in. "What else were they struggling for?"

"We're Just Vegetables"

"You always make out," said Jim, "that men are struggling for peace. That's where you are wrong. That's where all the world is wrong. It is the struggle that is life, not the peace they gain. I can prove it by showing you all through history that as soon as men gained one thing, they immediately got restless and started struggling for something else. Struggle is life. Not any goal. That is why the world is so sick and weary right now. They are in no mood for struggling. As soon as they get rested up a little from that last big struggle, the war, why, we'll all be happy again, struggling for something else."

"You make men out awfully restless," I said uneasily.

"Are you one of those," demanded Jim, "that dreams of a millennium in which there will be no more struggle, no more oppression, no more competition, but all mankind will live under his vine and fig tree in perfect peace?"

"Most certainly," I agreed.

"Then I hope you choke on a fig!" declared Jim. "If ever a millennium comes, it will be after the last man has vanished from the earth."

"Goodness," I cried, "what are we living for then?"

"For life!" shouted Jimmie, leaping up and pacing around his studio. "For action, struggle, contest, thrill! To feel our blood in our veins. To use our wits. To gain. To lose. To battle with the unknown. That's why I am jealous of garment workers and mill hands. They're the lucky ones; not us comfortable middle classers. They're the ones that are living. We're just vegetables!"

I sat watching him prowling up and down. I began to feel like a vegetable. Like a turnip. Or a rutabaga. I could not feel any blood in my veins, I just felt sort of dull and thick.

"Jimmie," I said, "what we need is a little exercise. We should go to some of those classes for obese business men at the gym."

"In the history of the world," cried Jim, "there has never been a more interesting age than this. We could join parties. We could meet in cellars. We could start things stirring that would ring through all time. Men of action are needed to-day more than in the time of Nero!"

"I was up at the gym one time," I said, "and I saw a class of nearly a hundred men, between fifty and sixty years of age, lying on their backs with their legs sticking up in the air."

"Francois Villon was a poet," cried Jimmie, as if he hadn't heard me at all. "A poet is no better than an artist or a writer. Yet the name of Francois Villon lives forever because, with his comrades of the Fir Cone Tavern, he led the patriots against the Duke of Burgundy."

"Isn't it a pity there aren't any taverns like the Fir Cone Tavern any more?" I asked. "With mendicant friars in the chimney corners, and the King with his cap fringed with little leaden images of the saints, sitting in disguise and listening to us plotting?"

"You aren't paying any attention!" shouted Jimmie. "Why don't you get hot? What's the matter with you? Sitting there like a turnip!"

I got up. No turnip can stand up.

"Life is passing you by," went on Jim more politely. "Let's do something. Let's go out and start something. Let's kick something over. Let's chase a cop!"

"What would we do when we caught him?" I asked.

"Ach!" exclaimed Jimmie, snatching his coat and jamming on his hat.

"Where are you off to?" I asked.

But he just rushed out the hall. And I after him. His jaw was set, his eyes flaming. He would not speak to me. We got in the elevator and went to the street. He strode from the building and turned west on King St. I had to hurry to keep up with him.

"Jimmie," I said, "if there is anything I can do?"

He kept striding along, muttering.

At a hot pace, we walked past Simcoe, past John, right to Spadina Ave. before Jimmie slowed up and looked down at me.

"Jimmie," I said, breathing fast, "what mischief are you up to? What's gone wrong with you?"

"I," declared Jim, in a soft, hissing voice, "am going to look for action! I am going up Spadina and find a strike."

"What kind of a strike?" I asked.

"There are all kinds of strikes," said Jim. "We'll find one up Spadina here somewhere. If you are game, come with me. If you are contented to be a bump on a long, go back. Leave me."

"I would hate," I admitted, "to be a turnip."

"Then follow me," said Jim.

We turned up our coats to hide our white collars so that we would not be mistaken for the white collar class. We stopped at Adelaide St. and looked east and west, and though there were plenty of factories, we could see no mobs of strikers. We marched to Richmond. Again we halted and gazed east and west. There were still more factories, large and small, but not a sign of any class struggle. At Queen St. we halted amidst a busy throng, and studied the faces of the people, all dark and deeply lost in thought, they were. We saw one small mob and we hurried to it, standing in front of a vacant store. But the speaker was not exhorting the masses. He was just selling a new kind of sharpener for safety razor blades.

Jim led on up Spadina a block or two, but any garment workers we saw were two or three hurrying in a most business-like and almost eager fashion with half-finished garments over their arms.

"They look happy enough," I said to Jim.

He merely turned on his heel and led me back to Queen. Along Queen he strode, eastward, back the direction we had come.

"All through here," said Jim, "according to the police, there are cellars full of malcontents, schemers, plotters!"

But no matter how attentively we looked, all we could

see were people in front of factories and stores talking about business.

"Let us put on a sinister and mysterious look," I suggested to Jimmie, "and maybe some of the plotters will mistake us for themselves and invite us into a cellar."

We tried, but all that happened was a panhandler came up to us and bummed ten cents off each of us.

"Not fierce enough," I said to Jim.

But at that moment, down a side street, we beheld what we were seeking.

A mob!

In front of a big factory, a throng of men and women, pushing, milling, heaving and shoving.

"Ah!" cried Jim, buttoning his coat and bracing his shoulders.

I came after him. A little in the rear.

"The masses," said Jim. "In revolt!"

Everyone Has Impulses

"Jimmie!" I cried. "Think before you commit yourself! Couldn't you take up curling! Or golf? Can't you content yourself with white collar amusements?"

But Jimmie was fairly leaping for the fray.

As we approached, there were half a hundred men and women milling about the factory doors. Their faces were set and grim. They were thrusting and weaving and all were talking and shouting at once.

We circled the mob and started to get in front of them, near the factory doors.

"Men and women!" shouted Jim, holding up his hand.

"Get back in your place!" shouted an excited man at the front of the mob.

"We wish to help you!" shouted Jimmie.

"What you need," I shouted, explanatorily, "is intelligent leadership!"

Three men from the front of the mob moved suddenly out and started for us. We backed up.

"You don't understand!" we yelled.

They chased us. We retreated to the back of the mob until the three had darted back into their position near the doors.

44

"Comrades!" bellowed Jimmie, walking cautiously toward the head of the throng.

This time a quite large man made a sudden dash out of the mob and he tripped Jimmie and then took me by the overcoat and lifted and tossed me brutally into the air so that I fell on an undefended sector of my body on the hard cold pavement.

He picked up my hat and came over and handed it to me.

"Listen," he said, not unkindly, to Jimmie who was now bending over me, "you boys have simply got to get in line. There is no use you trying to crash in like this."

"We want to help you," said Jim. "We don't want to crash in. We will willingly take the brunt. We will fight in the front ranks."

Surprise spread all over the big fellow's face.

"If you want a job," he repeated firmly, "get in line."

"A job?" Jim and I said together.

"Yes, what else did you want?" asked the big chap. "There is twenty jobs going in this factory and if you want one of them, line up like the rest of us. But it won't be no use. There is too many ahead of you."

With which he left us and went back into the mob to take the place that the others had kept for him while he did his duty with us.

Jim sat down on the kerb beside me because I did not yet feel like getting up.

"They are not strikers," I said, "they are job seekers."

"Rioting for jobs," said Jim, sadly. "Look at them. Struggling for creature comforts."

"One must eat," I pointed out.

Jim turned down his coat collar. He exposed his white collar as if it were a banner. He straightened his hat and stood up. He dusted off his coat.

"I suppose," he said, "in times like these every one of us has his impulses."

"Sure, Jim," I sympathized, holding my hand up for a lift. "I've often had that pink feeling myself."

Jim took my hand and hauled me to my feet.

"Upsadaisy," he said.

Pageant

April 14, 1934

"This being the hundredth anniversary of your native city," said Jimmie Frise, "what part, if any, are you taking in the pageants, celebrations and so forth?"

"I'm a little afraid," I said, "that the people of Toronto are not much given to pageants and celebrations."

"Ah, you forget the Twelfth of July," retorted Jimmie.

"That," I said, "is only a section of the populace, and anyway, if I am any judge, the majority of the people of Toronto, Protestants like myself, are slightly more inclined to be irritated by the traffic tie-ups involved on that occasion than to be inflamed by the principles involved. Personally, although I have lived all my life in Toronto, I have never yet seen the Orange parade."

"You ought to see the Orange parade we have in Birdseye Centre," said Jim.

"It is beautiful to be capable of celebrations," I said. "I wish Toronto were a little less fishy about life. Let somebody start a celebration, and we always think he is either drunk, crazy or bigoted. I have my fears about this Centennial pageant. I sort of fear I won't see it."

"It's coming off all right," assured Jim.

"Yes, but I said I feared I wouldn't see it. What I mean is, I might feel too Torontoey that day to bother going to see it."

"You Toronto people are funny," said Jim.

"I admit it," I said. "But after all, God made us."

"I wonder," said Jim. "You know, we foreigners from Birdseye Centre, Belleville, Regina or Chipmunktook, Nova Scotia, can always tell a Torontonian by his dull, fishy eye. He always has the look as if he were afraid you were expecting him to invite you home to supper."

"Aw," I said.

"To put it in a nutshell," went on Jim, "he looks kind of hen-pecked."

46

Faster we swept on, around another bend . . . "Jimmie," I shouted, "We'll be swept out into the lake."

"Go on," I said. "We true Torontonians have been absorbing abuse like this for a hundred years. We can take it."

"Don't you ever feel like celebrating?" demanded Jim.

47

"Are you Torontonians always content to clump down to work in the morning, and then clump solemnly back home again? Isn't there ever a slight desire to let loose and enjoy yourself once in a while?"

"We've got the greatest annual exhibition in the world!" I stated loudly.

"To which you invite people from elsewhere to come and have fun," retorted Jim. "And you stand aside and look at them solemnly."

"How about our skating carnival?" I demanded hotly. "The foreign stars we invite here say there is nothing like it in the whole world."

"Of course it is a public carnival?" asked Jim.

"I see what you mean," I said.

Where is Our Color?

"Look at your downtown, so swiftly deserted at supper time," said Jim. "Look at your amusement beaches; the biggest thing you can think of is burning an old boat. Look at your theatres! Have you a municipal theatre? Have you bands in your parks? No, sir, you have a city which, after a hundred years, is run strictly on a money-making basis. Nothing is given for nothing. You are a city of shopkeepers, and you spend your time, when not at work, counting up your bank book!"

"Toronto is a city of homes," I said. "Something like eighty per cent of us own our own homes."

"What you mean to say," said Jim, "is that eighty per cent of you have mortgages on your homes."

"You are terrible," I said.

"All I am trying to do," Jim replied, "is rouse you out of your typical Toronto lethargy. I want to know why you, whose great-grandfather was born in the village of York, are doing nothing to celebrate your Centenary?"

"The celebration," I assured him, "is in the hands of a competent committee."

"There you are," cried Jim. "You should worry!"

"Well, what do you suggest?" I exclaimed. "Do you want all us native sons to form a parade and go marching through the streets performing fancy evolutions like the Shriners?"

"That would be better than sitting back and showing no pride in your city at all," said Jim.

"Well, you see, Toronto does not go back to really picturesque times," I explained. "My ancestor was a watchmaker. And I had other ancestors who were farmers and masons and missionaries to the Indians. But they dressed much as we do. They worked all day the way we do. They were born, they lived and they died. Toronto's hundred years is not particularly romantic or colorful. I don't see how we can get a pageant out of it."

"Then why not go back a little further," said Jim. "You had plenty of color here before 1834. You had the great trail called the Carrying Place, which came out at the Humber river. It was the highway from the north up and down which passed war parties of the Iroquois ages ago. Down it came the Hurons with their packs of furs they had bartered from the Algonquins to trade to the Indians of the south. French voyageurs first saw Lake Ontario by coming down from Georgian Bay over the Carrying Place and landing out at the Humber. Up that trail went British war parties, Colonel Butler and his Devils; down it came the French war parties. Saint Jean de Brébeuf himself walked down the Carrying Place from his mission amongst the Hurons, and has actually trod the soil of Toronto. No color, no romance!"

"I had forgotten that," I admitted.

"And you had forts here in Toronto, nearly a hundred years before there was a Toronto, but none the less they belong to your story," said Jim.

"We may get some Indians into our pageant," I agreed.

"And coureurs de bois, and French adventurers, and British traders working in from the south," cried Jim. "Why, this city is filled with all the shadows of color!"

"I see it," I said.

Civic Pride Swells

"But what will you do about it?" demanded Jim. "How about your children? Are they to be brought up in the notion that there is nothing in life but a mortgage? The ideal of the true Torontonian, a house with a mortgage, the beginning and the end!"

"I never thought of it that way," I said.

"Conceal from them the very thought that once upon a time this very earth, of which you are anxious they should acquire a thirty or forty foot frontage, once was trod by adventurous white men, clad in skins of wild beasts, in bright tunics and gold-laced hats, with Indian bands at their command!"

My eyes glowed.

"Ah," said Jimmie, "I wish I were Toronto-born! I'd show you a pageant of pride."

"Do you suppose my children would be interested?" I asked. "I imagine they are a little too practical for pageants."

"Here we are," said Jim, "living on the banks of the Humber. Who knows but that the Carrying Place, that great portage from Lake Simcoe to Lake Ontario, did not pass right over the very ground we live on? All the children in the district would love a pageant. A pageant, say, of Etienne Brulé, the first white man to come down the Carrying Place and to see Lake Ontario and the site of Toronto."

"Yes?" I said.

"We could get a raft here somewhere on the Humber," went on Jimmie, "and you could be Etienne Brulé, dressed up in the old French fashion, and I could be your Indian guide. We could get aboard the raft and you could address the children on the shore, pretending they are savage Indians."

"So?" I said.

"You could in a few words tell them about the far country from which you have come, and then make a prophecy about the great city that one day would rise here."

"Wonderful, Jimmie!" I cried. "It would interest the children intensely. And at the same time, explain to them the story of the exploration of Canada."

"And give them pride in their own history," added Jim.

We went for a walk down by the Humber after an early supper and scouted the scene. We found the

Humber running rather high from heavy rains and thaws. But in one of the bends just below the Bloor St. bridge we found a sort of bay in the river where we could anchor a raft, and a nice dry bank where a number of children could sit for the pageant.

"I'll pretend I am your Indian guide," said Jim, "and I will keep steering and poling, as if we were travelling along."

"I can stand on the raft and make the speech, and at the end of it, unfurl a big flag."

"The French flag?" asked Jimmie.

"No," I said, after reflection. "It had better be the Union Jack so as not to confuse the children."

"Seeing we are on a raft," said Jim, "it could be the Canadian ensign."

"Very well," said I.

On a Raft on the Humber

Jimmie and I have the same gardener, and he very kindly undertook the raft part of the pageant, getting logs and planks, and he built on the Humber bank a very sturdy little raft. Being experts at costumes, Jim and I soon rigged out a suitable French outfit for me, and Jimmie dyed a suit of underwear an Indian tan, it being still too chilly for mere grease paint. I don't know what Etienne Brulé looked like, but I am sure if he was a smallish gentleman, he looked something like myself when I got into the plumed hat and gallant tunic of green plush. It isn't hard to look like an Indian. They all look the same. So Jimmie with his underwear and feathers looked like the chief of the Hurons. But we couldn't find a flag.

We told our children to inform a select group of the children of the neighborhood, but when we got out of the car and walked down the Humber banks Saturday afternoon, we were surprised to see what a fine turnout we had. There must have been forty.

I had written a suitable address which I memorized. It was Brulé addressing the savages and foretelling the coming of the white man and the great cities that would rise in days to come.

The Humber was running livelier than the last time

we saw it. In fact, I said to Jimmie that perhaps we had better do our act on the land, as the raft seemed to be tugging at its moorings, which were clothes-lines. But Jim and his water spaniel, old Rusty, stalked on board the raft. The children cheered as I stepped aboard.

"Now, children," I said loudly, "we are going to stage a pageant in honor of Toronto's Centenary. Does anyone know what Centenary means?"

One little boy said he knew.

"It means a buck," he said.

"A buck?"

"One hundred cents, one buck," said the little boy flatly.

So I had to go back over the ground a bit and explain about Centenary.

"Now, children," I said, "you pretend you are savage Indians gathered here along the river to watch a wonderful sight go by. It is a white man, a Frenchman, by the name of Étienne Brulé, the very first white man ever to see this land we live on, the site of Toronto. This is my Indian guide from far up on Lake Simcoe."

"I have a cottage on Lake Simcoe," announced one of the little boys.

"Now, now," I said. "So in my speech I shall tell you of the far country of the white man and of the great cities that some day will rise . . ."

"Are you going to talk French or Indian?" asked a larger boy.

"Now, now," I said. "Now, now, children!"

Like Real Pioneers

One small boy who had been down at the water's edge dipping his foot in and obviously trying to get on the raft, and whom I had been pushing back quietly, suddenly cried out:

"Come up and see us sometime, Mr. Brooley!"

And to my horror, he tossed up at me the landward end of the rope. He had untied the mooring from the peg on shore.

"Hey!" I shouted to Jimmie.

But the raft just swept around in the current. I sat

down for safety and watched with horror as the second rope tightened and slowly, slowly the second peg drew loose out of the soft bank of the Humber.

"Help!" I bellowed. But the little children all just sat there and looked with delight at the raft and its picturesque freight.

Jim heaved and poled with his long clothes prop. I sat and gripped the raft and felt the cold Humber sopping into my plush breeches.

"Make for shore," I commanded frantically.

"I'm doing—my best!" grunted Jimmie, heaving.

But down and around the bend we swept, with a stream of children running along the bank cheering us out of sight.

"Jimmie," I shouted, as we rounded another bend, "we'll be swept out into the lake and starve to death."

Faster we swept on, around another bend and into a still, swift passage of the river where sundry sucker fishermen sitting along the shore with their dip nets eyed us with astonishment.

"Paddle with your pole," I said. "Make for shore."

"It's too deep here to pole," said Jim. "We're drifting to the bank."

"What a mess!" I remarked.

"No," said Jim. "This is very interesting. Most pageants, like most paintings and pictures, show us these early explorers and pioneers sailing grandly down our noble rivers, dressed in fine clothes, and with one knee bent, staring ahead."

"Well?" I said.

"Well," went on Jimmie, "I think we are right now demonstrating how these pioneers and explorers, these Champlains and Brulés and La Salles really did come down these rivers. I mean, with the seat of their pants wet, and pretty badly scared and the rafts and canoes kind of tippy and not knowing where they were headed. You know?"

"Yes," I said, "I know."

"In fact," went on Jim, "our little pageant is likely to be more realistic than Toronto's big one."

And then the raft touched shore.

Politics

June 16, 1934

"What part," asked Jimmie Frise, "are you taking in
the coming elections?"

"I'm afraid," I admitted, "I am not much at politics.
Politics seem to have died out in this generation. I've
heard how my grandfather, Willie Greig, used to sit on
his horse at the crossroads near his farm at Pickering far
into the winter night, shouting politics with his neighbor, also on a horse."

"Why on a horse?" asked Jim.

"So they couldn't fight," I explained. "It was agreed
between them never to talk politics when on foot."

"What party was your grandfather?" asked Jim.

"I couldn't say," I said.

"There you are!" cried Jimmie. "You know all about
the intensity of your grandfather's political feeling. But
you don't know whether he was a Grit or a Tory."

"I think a man like you," Jim went on, "would go well
in politics. You have a soft, kind look. People would trust
you."

"I've often thought of entering public life," I said,
"that is, if I ever got ahead a little at the bank and had
the time to spare."

"I bet you could make a great political speech," went
on Jim.

"Ahem," I said. "I talk easily."

"What this country needs," pursued Jim, "are politicians who will look out for the common man. Men without big ideas of themselves. Men who will serve, with
courage and devotion, the interests of the mass of the
people. You are such a man."

54

"Nonsense, Jimmie," I cried. "You are the man! You have described yourself to a tee. Modest, honest and always interested in the common man. You should go into politics."

"But I can't talk," explained Jimmie. "I may have sound ideas, but I can't express them. Whereas, however unsound your ideas, your expression of them is excellent."

"We might," I surmised, "enter public life together: you to provide the character and ideas and I to express them. We could get seats beside each other in parliament and you could mumble at me while I stood up and made fiery orations. My prompter."

"I wonder," asked Jim, "if it is too late to get in on this

55

election? It seems to me you can't run unless you are entered."

"We could start by attending some meetings," I suggested, "and if we make a hit with the people they will insist on us running."

Country Meetings are Best

"I wonder where there are any meetings?" mused Jim.

"Why, there are meetings all over, in schools and dance halls, everywhere." I said.

"I have a hunch," said Jim, "that we ought not to start at city meetings at all. Let's go out to country meetings. We would show up better there. After all, we are more country than city, aren't we?"

"That's a wonderful suggestion," I assured him. "Our sympathies are with the country people. Country folk can detect real worth in people far more quickly than city people. City people are dumb. They are so used to being bamboozled, horn-swoggled and high-pressured they can't tell the genuine article when they do see it."

"Then we can drive out to the country after supper and attend a meeting in one of the little towns near Toronto," decided Jim. "Country meetings are quieter and not so well organized as city meetings. You will be able to find a spot to get to your feet easier in a nice, slow-going country meeting than at one of these cut-and-dried city meetings. Have you some good, high-sounding words to pull? Do you need to rehearse your speech? What will you talk on?"

"I always trust to the inspiration of the moment," I stated.

"Oh, by the way," asked Jim, "which party are we supporting?"

"We can decide that when we attend the meeting," I explained. "There is no use us deciding which side we are on until we can tell, from the tone of the meeting, which side the meeting is on. Then we horn in on the right side. It's to get elected we are doing this, isn't it?"

"Quite right," agreed Jim. "Well, you had better read

the papers to-day and get a line on the main arguments on both sides."

"I'll prepare two sets of notes," I suggested. "One for either side."

"Good," said Jim. "Work in a lot of phrases like 'This is a time of great change, of transmutation of all our former values into modern terms,' or 'Fellow citizens, at such a time as this, dare we, dare we tamper with those institutions which the generations of our fathers have, by their life and their death, proven to be sound?' You know the stuff."

"I get it," I said, anxious to be off to read the newspapers and get organized.

"Get some facts and figures, too," said Jim. "Some large millions, and look up a lot of words that mean embezzlement and fraud, without actually saying it."

"How's this: derelict in their sacred duty?" I tried.

"That's it!" cried Jimmie. "Derelict. Swell."

I spent part of the day reading the papers, and it was easy, by putting some of them on the table and the others on the bureau, to separate the political situation very simply and work up a collection of notes on both sides. I got some beautiful words. Machine. Chaotic. Quack medicines. Invasion of public rights. And so forth.

The Spirit of Battle

Jimmie called for me right after supper.

"James," I said, because if we went on the one side, we might have to favor titles, and Sir "Jimmie" is obviously out of the question, "James, which direction should we go?"

"Any direction," said Jim, "until we come to a public meeting in the country. And the country is full of them."

It looked like a thunderstorm as we left the city in a northwesterly direction. And we were scarcely in the country before one of those real old thunderstorms was in progress, in which every bolt of lightning seems to be directed, if not directly at you, at least to the lone elm tree which you are just passing.

"I hope we don't have too far to go," I said.

"Just nicely in the country," said Jim.

We passed through a couple of little villages, semi-suburban, where a few people loitered in the shelter of gas stations and gloom prevailed all otherwise.

We passed farmhouses in connection with which it was impossible to imagine politics.

"What do you suppose the political complexion of this neighborhood would be?" I asked.

"You never can tell in the country," explained Jimmie. "In the city, it does not matter to you what politics your neighbors entertain, or the people across the road. But out in the country, there are so many factors to decide your politics. For example, in the country, a man usually follows his father's politics. But if you don't like your neighbor, you hold the opposite political views from him. It is one of the ways of expressing your dislike for your neighbors."

"Perhaps it is not going to be easy," I suggested, "if we do succeed in finding a meeting, to discover which is the stronger side for us to be on."

"I'll advise you," said Jim.

Ahead we saw a village. And as we neared the village, Jim seemed to sense there was a political meeting here.

Just this side of the village was a big building all lighted up. And cars were parked densely around.

"Here we are!" cried Jim.

It was a handsome sort of building, one of these modern-looking community halls the country is starting to erect, and by the well-to-do look of the motor cars packed around it, this was a meeting of successful farmers, country gentlemen of the first rank.

"Boy," I breathed, "this would be the place to get our start in the world of politics! Look! Sport roadsters and everything!"

"Perhaps," said Jim, as we got out of the car in the rain, "there might be some of these big retired business men farmers at this meeting."

We hurried to the door, and as we entered, we sensed the tension, the spirit of battle, which filled the meeting. There were no loiterers in the lobby, and no young men smoking cigarettes in the corridor. Everybody was in the packed hall, and even the door was jammed with the backs of men straining forward to listen, while a voice boomed angrily amidst little gusts of clapping and occasional cheers.

Jim could see over the heads of the men jammed in the door, and he relayed the news to me.

"It's crowded," whispered Jim. "Jammed to the walls. I don't recognize the chairman. But there is certainly something doing here. Listen."

Loud cheers and boos and stamping of feet ended the remarks of the booming voice.

I could hear the chairman making some remarks, and then a new voice began. A strong, nasal, penetrating voice.

"Those of us who have been charged with the government of this . . ."

"BOOOOO! Miaaaoooww! Boo, boo!" came roars from the meeting, amidst hisses and feet stampings.

Jim caught my arm and led me to the outer door.

"You can see the meeting is against the government," exclaimed Jim excitedly. "There can be no doubt about those boos and hisses. Let's get in somehow, perhaps we can get in by a door or a window. And at the first opportunity, you jump up and start lambasting the government or something. At the top of your lungs. And don't forget to stick your clenched fist forward at arms length. A fighting posture. You know!"

"All right, all right," I agreed breathlessly. "Why can't we just push in past those fellows at the door?"

"The aisle is crowded, too," said Jim. "We'll have to get in somewhere that you can be seen. Let's scout."

We went outside in the rain and walked around the building. There were two side doors both locked. There was a back door, also locked, with a man inside who gestured us through the window to go away.

But up about ten feet was a small window, with the downpipe from the eavetrough running beside it. The water gurgled in the downpipe and from the open window above us streamed light and tumult and cigar smoke.

"Could we get in through there?" I asked.

"I imagine," said Jim, "that window is right at the back of the platform. We wouldn't want to land with a thump on the platform, would we?"

So, we went all around again without finding any other windows or doors, and we went inside the hall again and tried to wiggle through the jam at the door, but it was no use. And the meeting was getting hotter all the time.

"Jimmie," I said, "we'll simply have to climb through that window, platform or no platform. It will be a dramatic entry! It will certainly focus attention on us. And anyway, there are a lot of people on the platform, and they may screen our actual arrival."

So Jim hunted about and got an old table, a large lawn roller and an empty tar barrel, and with these we built a sort of ladder to reach the window. I got up first, and Jim came close behind, so as to help boost me through the window.

I peeped in. I saw, through a fog of smoke, a packed sea of faces, like pebbles on the shore. All eager. All excited and hot. In the near foreground, almost where I could touch them, were two rows of heads, mostly bald, with their backs to me. These were the gentlemen on the platform.

"How's she look?" hissed Jim.

"It's about a six-foot drop inside. If I can get through the window quickly, they will hardly notice me at all. I'll just drop in and sit on a chair until you get in. Then you come and sit calmly beside me, as if this was the way we always come to meetings. There are several empty chairs at the back of the platform, right under me here. Can you manage to get through all right?"

"I'll be right after you," said Jim.

It was raining more heavily.

"What I think," shouted the speaker with the nasal voice, amidst an uproar of feet and yells and boos, "of a lot of people like you, no gratitude, not a spark of gratitude for all the years we have faithfully served you . . .".

"Psst!" said Jim, just as I raised one leg to enter. "If I

were you, I would rush to the front of the platform and start your speech the instant you touch the floor."

I pulled myself together. I quickly slipped one leg over the window sill and swung the other one after, bounced to the floor, leaped across the platform, and thrusting through the row of men sitting on chairs, stuck my clenched fist out at the audience, who stared with open mouths and glaring eyes.

"Down," I roared, "with the government or something! How about the returned soldiers! Who kept the . . ."

"BOOOOOOOOO!" bellowed the crowd, rising to their feet.

It was all over in a minute. The chairman and several bald-headed men took me, while others surged on to the platform from the audience, and amidst an immense confusion I was carried across the platform to the window, hoisted up and dropped out.

Jimmie caught me.

The chairman stuck his head out of the window.

"Scat," he said. "Beat it, you Bolshevik!"

"Yes sir," said Jimmie.

We went around the building, where half a dozen younger men were waiting for us, having come out the front door. They looked at us curiously in the light from the porch.

"Which party is this meeting for?" asked Jim.

"Party?" asked the young men.

"Yes, which side are they on? Did the government call the meeting, or the opposition?" asked Jim.

"You've got the wrong place," said the young men. "This is the Twitchgrass Golf and Country Club, and they are holding their annual meeting."

"Oh, pardon," said Jim, "we thought it was a political meeting."

"No, there's a political meeting of some kind down in the county hall at the far end of the village," said they.

Jim and I got in the car.

"How about it?" asked Jim. "Will we go on down?"

"It's such a nasty night for politics," I said.

So we drove back home.

Tastefully Furnished

June 23, 1934

"Well," said Jimmie Frise, "it can't be put off any longer."

"What can't?" I inquired.

"Locating a summer cottage," said Jim. "I've been stalling it off for weeks, and now my family is about ready to go away for the summer. But where?"

"You should have no trouble," I assured him. "Up near our place, there must be a dozen attractive summer homes for rent this year. You just decide on a price you want to pay and then take the first one that fits."

"Oh is that so?" asked Jim. "I see you have never rented a cottage."

"No," I admitted. "We still have the one I was raised in from childhood; and then I married into another one."

"Well, that should break the monotony to some extent," said Jim.

"How do you mean?" I asked indignantly.

"I can't imagine anything more deadly than owning a summer cottage," said Jim. "You never get rid of it. You live in it generation after generation. It grows aged and infirm, but you cling to it grimly. Every tree, every stone, every berry bush becomes familiar to you, and you watch the bushes and trees changing with the years,

Over the rocks, down to the bouldery shore we
ran, our noses into the breeze. "Gentlemen!"
gasped our guide.

63

but no new ones ever come. You see the same people, the old ones aging, the young ones growing up to fulfill your worst expectations. The shingles curl, the veranda posts become decayed and punky. Floor boards grow weak and threaten always to collapse. But you cling to it still. No matter how you may move from place to place in the city, or from one city to another, no matter how your condition may alter in business or society, you still stick to the summer cottage. At last, when you can't bear it any longer, you rent it."

"Oh, come, come," I said.

"In all my years of exploring the summer cottage situation in this part of the world," said Jim, "I have never seen a new summer cottage. All summer cottages are old. There must have been a terrific cottage building boom about 1900."

"Where have you done most of your looking for summer cottages?" I demanded.

"All over," said Jim. "But I don't expect anything different. I'll go out this week-end and drive around the old familiar summer resorts, Lake Simcoe, Balsam Lake, Muskoka. And I'll end up by renting, as usual, some mouse-infested, dead leaf filled, musty, mouldy, hand-me-down old fire trap of a cottage, and at least we will be better off than those who own cottages and are condemned to suffer the same one year after year."

"Have you asked your friends?" I inquired.

"You can't tell by them," said Jim. "Comfortably furnished cottage, they say, in select neighborhood, bathing, two rowboats. That's the last one I heard about. And when I got there, it was comfortable, in so far as it had chairs to sit on, though somewhat warped. There was bathing, if you wanted to sprain your ankle by wading amongst slimy boulders. There were two rowboats, but both of them were sunk in the ramshackle boathouse which the ice had all but washed away."

"You are just pessimistic," I assured Jim. "There are hundreds of delightful cottages."

Pictures of Lord Roberts

"There were funny old cracked dishes and pictures of

Lord Roberts tacked to the walls," went on Jim, gloomily. "And another picture of Queen Victoria, sitting, with King Edward, then the Prince of Wales, standing stoutly behind her chair. The mirrors in the different rooms made your face look comic."

"How much was it?" I asked.

"For the season, $150," said Jim.

"Very reasonable," I said. "Lots of the better class summer cottages cost from $600 to $1,000 for the two months. But I see you have a prejudice in this matter. You start out with the fatalistic feeling that you will be disappointed. I'd be glad to help you find a cottage. I am lucky, because I am cheerful. I expect to be pleased. And I am. It always works."

"You might make a big success," suggested Jim, "going about solving problems for pessimistic people. A professional. Like a water diviner."

"I still believe," I said, "that if you go expecting to be pleased, you are much more likely to find what you want than if you go expecting to be disappointed."

"Let's look at an agent's list and see if there are any cottages," suggested Jim, working away at his drawing board. So I procured a list of summer cottages for rent. Small ones, large ones, from $10 a week to $500 a month. Some with nothing but a beautiful vista. Others with hot and cold running water, double garage, sleeping quarters over the boat house, motor launch if desired, and so forth.

"How would $100 a month catch you?" I asked Jim.

"Too high," said Jim. "Let's hear something around $50 a month."

"You mustn't forget," I pointed out, "that the two months' rent is all the owner gets for the whole year."

"After paying $900 for it in the reign of King Edward," said Jim, "and then raising all his own family there and three lots of grandchildren until it is entirely worn out from use, how much return should a man expect from his investment in a summer cottage?"

"There is the sentimental value," I argued.

"What have you got there at $50 a month?" asked

Jim.

I read down the list, and came to three at $50 a month. One was near the city, only 11 miles out.

"Probably an abandoned chicken ranch," said Jim.

The next one was at Lake Simcoe.

"Probably the one we were in last season," muttered Jim.

The third one was in Muskoka, beautifully situated, tastefully furnished, most exclusive neighborhood, boating, bathing, fishing. Only careful tenant need apply.

"Ha, ha," said Jimmie. "Careful not to step too heavy!"

"Jim," I said, "I like the sound of that one. Tastefully furnished."

"Faded Chinese lanterns hanging from the rough board ceiling of the living room," sneered Jim.

"Beautifully situated," I read.

"In a bed of poison ivy," suggested Jim.

"Somehow," I said, "this one gives me a hunch. I'd be glad to run up with you and lend you my good luck."

Before McKinley was Shot

So we called up the telephone of the Toronto gentleman who was offering the cottage for sale, and agreed to meet him in the Muskoka village on Saturday and he would guide us in to see it. A lovely drive up Yonge St., with that happy early season feeling, when the roads seem to sing under your wheels and none of the trees are faded or dusty, and all the girls have new sailor trousers.

We met the gentleman in the village and he got in our car and guided us down roads that got narrower and wilder until we came out on the lake.

"It's just a short walk in from here," said the gentleman. "We have always resisted any idea of running the road any farther than this. I don't want any motor traffic whizzing past my sylvan retreat. Don't you think so?"

"There wouldn't be much whizzing on this road," said Jim.

We walked for ten or fifteen minutes along paths, along the beach, climbing over rocks and driftwood and pushing through thickets.

"Here we are," cried the gentleman.

There were six cottages in a row, all closely spaced beside one another. They were rather aged.

"Which one?" asked Jim, glumly.

"The fourth one," said the gentleman, gaily. "Ah, I hate to let it go, you can have no idea what this little place means to my family! But with the girls all grown up and wanting to go to Europe and so forth."

We walked along the rocks in front of the row and stepped on to the faded veranda of the fourth cottage. You could step from the veranda of one to the veranda of the others.

"With all the room in Muskoka," said Jim, "why do they build the cottages in huddles like this?"

"Ah, you have no idea what lovely neighbors these are," said the gentleman. "The bonfires at night, the singing, the wiener roasts. It's just a little community. The women folk prefer this to lonely cottages spaced far apart. We feel sorry for those people who own islands. One lonely cottage on an island. Don't you think so?"

We examined the cottage. The veranda posts were still firm. But the railing had been patched. There were broad stains under the roof where leaks occurred. The screens were gray and had holes. When the gentleman opened the door, having considerable difficulty with the key, the familiar cottage smell smote us. Into the dark interior we stepped, and the gentleman walked over and drew a blind a little way. How thoroughly the ladies close up the cottage, little caring what a desolate view is to meet the eye in the summer to come! Wash tubs upside down on the living room floor. Mattresses suspended on wire clothes lines, mice nests on the chair, for always one cushion is forgotten at the last minute.

"Stuffy, isn't it?" said the gentleman. "But a cottage always smells stuffy after being closed all winter."

The floor was littered with leaves, and somebody else will have to figure how those leaves get in.

Jim stepped gingerly and doubtfully from room to room.

"Ah," said he, pointing to a picture of Lord Roberts in

67

scarlet tunic tacked to a bedroom wall.

Nice people had lived in this cottage. There were old-fashioned things tacked to the walls, and no matter how faded they had become, nice people had been too in love with the years that had gone to tear them down. There were frayed palm fans scrawled with names. Picture postcards, dim with age. Funny looking wall vases with Muskoka painted on them. Bulrushes that must have been sprayed upon that wall before McKinley was shot.

There were home-made cabinets in the dining room and kitchen. The chairs around the table were all odd. There was a high chair, specially faded and worn.

A mouse skittered across the kitchen.

"Dear, dear, the first mouse I ever saw in here," said the gentleman.

"What is that other smell?" asked Jim.

And there was indeed another smell.

"This Muskoka breeze will soon rid the cottage of that stuffy air," said the gentleman. "Now, come around here to the back and I'll show you the best part of the whole place. It is the envy of all your neighbors. A stone cellar! Yes, sir. A solid stone cellar, not large, you understand, but what a convenience for the women. It keeps food perfectly. No matter how often the supply boat fails to come, no matter how the cows of the man who supplies the milk may stray, you can count on this cellar to keep a good supply of perishable food in perfect condition."

We went under the cottage at the back. There was a dark cavern, in which stones cemented together formed a wall with a wooden door in it. The door was ajar.

The gentleman went first. Jim followed. I brought up the rear.

The gentleman scratched a match. There were wild shouts, yells, and a stampede, I leading. And the dense and brand new odor of skunk billowed out past us no matter how fast we travelled.

Out the back, over the rocks, down to the bouldery shore we ran, noses into the breeze.

"Gentlemen," gasped our guide, "how unfortunate! I hope you escaped."

"We can't tell for a while yet," said Jim.

"Perhaps if we waited a little while, the animal would go away and I could show you more fully . . ."

"Is this the bathing beach?" asked Jim.

"There is a good beach about half a mile down the shore," said the gentleman. "Just a nice walk."

"I'm afraid," said Jim, "that I must have a beach right in front of my cottage. That is one thing my family insists on."

"In that case—" said the gentleman.

So he went up and locked the doors very softly and carefully while we waited in the breeze. We drove him back to the village and Jim and I went home in the evening.

We were conscious of a faint odor, our cigarettes tasted queer, and the attendants at the gas station at Orillia looked at us oddly. But you soon get used to anything. Especially if you are a summer cottage owner.

"Well," said Jim, "you didn't divine a skunk when you divined that cottage for me?"

"The skunk," I said, "saved you from accepting the cottage. You might have taken the cottage in sheer boredom if there hadn't been that skunk. I am lucky. My luck even provides skunks."

"You have a wonderful philosophy," admitted Jim.

"How would you like to drive home down around the other side of Lake Simcoe," I asked, "and we could look over some of the cottage resorts in passing?"

"No," said Jim. "I have been through all this before. It's just the same old thing. At last, in desperation, we'll take a cottage by mail or long distance telephone. And when we get there, it will be painted gray, with old initials carved in the veranda posts, and 1904 carved under them, and there will be a swamp in front and a big empty stoney field behind, and the man who delivers the ice will be very intemperate and everybody on the point will be nervous of him. And the mosquitoes will be bad until the 20th of July, and in August the family will lie around reading last year's magazines, getting crankier and crankier and wanting to come home to the city."

"Jim," I accused, "you are a complete pessimist."

"No," said Jim. "I'm just an average Canadian."

Sea Dogs

July 7, 1934

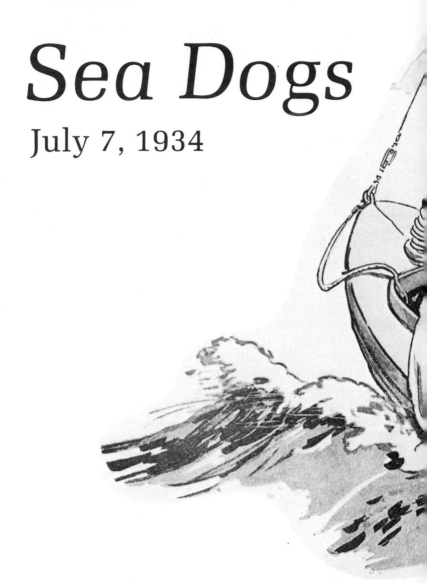

"What a day," cried Jimmie Frise, "for sailing!"

We were up in his studio in the attic of The Star building, looking out his windows over the wide sparkling blue lake and Toronto bay, with its steamers and tugs and launches, like toy ships slowly puffing across the crinkled azure.

As I scrambled from under the wet canvas, I made a wild grab at the buoy.

"I've never done any sailing," I said. "Curious, isn't it, how few Ontario people go in for water sports, with all this vast inland sea at their disposal?"

"One-third the surface of Ontario," said Jim, "is water."

"You would think," I said, "that we central Canadians would be a naval, a maritime, a sea-going race of people."

"I can't understand it," cried Jimmie. "Look at that water—miles, leagues of open sea, ready for the adventurous man to drive the bow of his little ship on glorious, health-glowing cruises!"

"Is it fear, do you suppose?" I asked. "A lot of us have a deep inborn fear of water."

"Fear!" snorted Jim. "What is there to fear on water? You have a tight little ship under you, and you have mastered the simple art of sailing a small craft, and what can happen to you?"

"I've heard some terrible squalls can blow up on these great lakes in a few minutes," I said.

"Pshaw," said Jim, "for six years before the war I owned a fourteen-foot dinghy and I've sailed from May to October all over the lake, down to Oshawa, up to Hamilton, right across to Niagara, and I've seen some great squalls in my time. . . ."

"How did you come to quit sailing?" I exclaimed. "I never knew you had been a sailor."

"Oh," said Jim, "after the war I got married and I had expenses and then my family arrived, and you can't really go sailing and neglect a small family. But, by Jove, now that my family is growing up, I've a good notion to take up sailing again. Perhaps a little bigger craft than a dinghy. Maybe one of these small sloops."

"It must be grand sport," I said.

"Man," assured Jimmie, "there is no sensation in the world, not even flying, to compare with leaping across a spanking blue sea, with plenty of white crests, in a trim little ship. Nothing to compare. There is exercise in it, the straining of the sheets, the handling of the tiller, the sense of poise as you balance ship against wind. The purity of the cold, rushing water. The purity of the air. I can't understand why we Ontario people are so indifferent to a sport that surely all the rest of the world must envy us."

"Maybe everybody else is busy with young families and the cares of business," I suggested. "After all, you can't go for a sail the way you can go for a game of golf. On the spur of the moment."

"Certainly you can," claimed Jim. "No matter what the weather, you can scoot down to the waterfront, run out your boat and be skimming across the lake in less time than it would take you to motor to the golf club."

Good Fun in Any Weather

"But the weather has a lot to do with it?" I asked.

"You get to love the experience of different kinds of weather," said Jim. "Westerlies are best. But there is a kick in going out in one of those gray easterlies. And still another kind of pleasure is drooping along in one of those hot, calm days with a little fitful breeze. It is good fun in any weather. How I'd love to be out there this minute!"

"I had ancestors who were great sea dogs," I said. "Sometimes I can feel their blood stirring in my veins. I had ancestors by the name of Buhonin or Buchanan—they couldn't spell, so we're not sure how you spell it—who owned the sailing ship my ancestors came to Canada in a hundred and fifty years ago. Alex Buhonin. They were great sailors. It took them only sixteen weeks to come from Cork to Quebec."

"I'd like to be out on that lake right now," mused Jimmie.

"Sometimes," I said, "when there is a great storm blowing, I love to go down to the breakwater off Sunnyside and stand on the shore and watch the immense seas bursting in. My blood seems to boil with excitement. I really believe I have the blood of sea-dogs in me."

"I wonder," said Jim softly, "if old Eddie still has a dinghy? Or Harry Moyer? It would be fun to sit at the tiller of a dinghy once again."

"As true Ontarians," I suggested, "we ought not to let the cult of the sea, or of the great lakes, die out."

Jimmie went to the telephone. He called Eddie somebody, who seemed to do a lot of laughing, and he had no dinghy. Neither did Harry Moyer. But the third call, a man named Slim somebody, said he still owned a dinghy down in a boathouse at the waterfront, but it hadn't been out for two years and it would probably need a lot of calking.

"I have a friend who can bail," explained Jimmie over the telephone. And his friend Slim told him to get the key from some old watchman who was down around the boathouses.

"Come on," cried Jim, all flushed with excitement. "We're going sailing right now."

"These Buhonins," I explained to Jim as we went down in the elevator, "were not direct ancestors of mine. They were sort of great uncles."

Jim drove us down to the waterfront and easterly to a place where there were a great many tumble-down old boathouses and sheds, all very rickety and staggered, and amongst them we found a lean, aged man who silently handed Jim the keys and showed him one of the ricketiest of all the boathouses. Inside the gloom, we located Slim's dinghy by a number painted on it. It was dusty. Its mast was out and its sail was rolled around the spars, and brown paper had been tied around them; but the mice had been at the paper.

"She looks pretty antique to me," I suggested.

"She's a great old stepper," said Jim, lifting mast and sail and all, and carrying them to the boathouse door.

Just a Little Bailing

We dragged the dinghy out the door and rolled it on small logs to the water's edge. We had to push scum and things aside to make a launching space in the bay. Then Jim stepped the mast, as he termed it, and presently unfurled the sail and hoisted it.

"It looks kind of rotten to me," I suggested.

Jim examined the wooden rings around the mast, and the ropes, all of which seemed aged and infirm to my landsman's eye. But Jim was all excitement.

"Great shape," said he. "Considering she has been laid up two seasons."

"And how old was she before that?" I inquired.

"I forget when she was launched," said Jim, "but she's

A1 at Lloyds."

He hunted about amongst the tumbledown shanties and sheds and found a battered paint pail.

"This is yours," said Jim, presenting me with the pail. "At first, being dry, she is likely to leak a little at the seams. But in an hour or so she will tighten up nicely. You'll have to do a little bailing. Do you mind?"

"One thing our Buhonin blood was good at," I assured Jim, "was manning the pumps."

"Heave-ho," said Jimmie. "Get aboard and I'll shove her off."

He shoved her off and lowered the centre board. It took some hammering, and it seemed to me the centre board might drop right out of her, but before I could come to any opinion, we were sailing, and Jim had the shabby old sail full of the bright west wind, and we were heeling mildly and headed for Centre Island.

"What do you think of this!" cried Jim leaning out backwards. "Get to your pumps."

Clear rivulets of water were pouring in under the grated flooring of the dinghy. The waves slapped her sides with music. The mast and spars creaked and the sail spanked gaily. And as soon as there was enough water at the back end of the flooring, I started to bail. It was easy. Three canfuls, and I was ahead of the game and could sit back and admire the scenery for three minutes before I had to scoop another three canfuls.

"We'll go out the eastern gap, mate," hailed Jim.

"Aye, aye, sir," I replied, bailing another three canfuls.

The city receded and we came to the great concrete gap that is so much longer than it looks from shore. The west wind carried us through the gap at a spanking pace, and as we came to the outer end, a swell began to lift us.

"Do you think she is in shape for deep sea going?" I hailed the master.

"Belay your spavins, mate," shouted Jim. "Get abaft the binnacle and bail."

Bigger and Greener Waves

We popped out the gap into the open lake, and instead

of little slapping waves there were big, long, hurried waves all going some place. Straight east, straight for Scarboro, Kingston and points east, the long, green waves were hurrying, with excited foaming tops.

The dinghy climbed right on to them and into them. With much louder creaks and much noisier spanks of the sail, she climbed ahead into the big four-foot waves with the windy tops, and one minute she would be on top of one and then in the hollow of the next one, and sometimes they would curl and hiss right under the seat of my pants, because Jimmie had ordered me on deck.

"Sit up here on the decking," he roared, "and when I lean back you lean back. Don't go overboard."

"Aye, aye, sir," I replied.

The mast and the spars creaked and screeched. The sail slatted and the dinghy bottom would come down violently into gullies in the water.

"She's making water, cap'n," I hailed.

"Man the pumps," commanded Jimmie, leaning far out.

"We're out clear of the island, Jim," I said, leaning near him. "The wind's getting fresher."

"She'll be good in another couple of miles," agreed Jim.

The waves grew longer and wider apart and higher. We were running across them, and when we went down in the valley of one, the sail would slat, and when we came up on the top of the next one, the sail would fill and she'd lean far down.

Jim was studying the sail and ropes above.

"Anything wrong?" I asked, looking about the heaving seas, where not a sail was to be seen, not a speck of smoke on the horizon, and the city was small and far behind and even the island was dropping low.

But Jim just stared at the sail and drew gently on the mainsheet.

Far ahead I saw a red buoy heaving and falling in the sea. I pointed.

"Shoal ahead," I hailed.

"Steamer channel," replied Jim.

"How about turning now?" I asked. "I'm getting chilly, Jim."

"Man the pumps," said Jim. "I am a little afraid to bring her about. See that pulley up aloft?"

I could see a pulley but it looked all right to me.

"One good yank, and the halyard through that pulley will come apart," said Jim.

The wind was still fresher. The waves longer, livelier, greener. Sometimes a whole quart would skitter off the top of one of them and spray Jim and me and the sail.

"Uv-uv-uv-uv-uv," I shivered. "Let's turn."

The buoy was coming nigh. We kept steadily at it, and we came abreast of it, Jim roared:

"Ready about!"

I ducked.

We slammed around the buoy, the sail fluttered into the wind, Jim laid the tiller hard over, and down fell the sail, gaff, boom, halyard and all.

"Pull her in," roared Jim. "Grab the buoy!"

And as I scrambled from under the wet canvas, I felt the dinghy bump the buoy. I made a wild grab at a rusty, ungrabbable surface, and then I felt my hand touch an iron ring. I clutched.

In a jiffy, Jim had a rope out and through the ring. In two more jiffies, we had the sail all safely tucked aboard, with none hanging over; and there we were, rising and falling, rising and falling, fast to the big iron buoy.

"Jim," I gasped, "what do we do now?"

"This is nothing," said Jim. "All I do now is unstep the mast and rig a new halyard. It won't take half an hour."

"I have an engagement for dinner," I told Jim.

But unstepping the mast out there with a big sea running and an iron buoy rising and falling lazily, was not so easy. Jim had me help balance him as he tried to stand on the dinghy bow to unstep the mast. He heaved and jerked and tugged.

"H'm," said he. "Swelled, I guess."

"How?" I asked, balancing. I felt rather queer. The big buoy was so lazy. Every time it sank, I felt like an elevator in my stomach.

"She's been dry so long, I guess the mast has swelled a little. We'll try later, when it gets a little quieter."

"Ug," I said. "Pardon me."

"What is it?" asked Jim. "You're kind of green."

"That buoy," I said. "Ug, pardon me. It heaves so."

As we and the dinghy rose, the big rusty buoy fell. As we fell, the buoy rose.

"Phew," said I.

"Here," said Jim. "Bail. It will do you good."

I bailed but it did me no good. I began to feel as if nothing mattered. I looked back toward Toronto, small and bright on the skyline, and I sneered.

"Phew," I said. "Phew."

The wind did not quiet. West winds don't do that. They love the afternoon and the early evening. They seem to go boyish about 5 p.m.

"Here," said Jim, "lie down in the stern."

But lying down did not help. It only made it seem worse. The shadowy bulk of the buoy pitched and rolled sickeningly. The dinghy bobbed and fell beside it.

"Isn't this swell?" said Jim leaning back and surveying the waste of waters. "I love mishaps. They make things memorable. If we had just gone sailing, and nothing had happened, we would have forgotten all this in a year."

But I interrupted him. I kept on interrupting him for quite a little while.

"How is the old Buhonin blood?" asked Jim, after I had got quiet. But I could think of nothing to say.

I drowsed. I moaned and groaned. Every time I opened a crack of my eye, there heaved the vast brown buoy, up, and we up after it; and then it heaved down, and down came we.

"Sail ho," cried Jim.

I sat up weakly. There a little way off, another dinghy was spanking past. They waved. They turned and came over to us. A mere slip of a girl in sailor pants handled the dinghy smartly and brought it within a few feet.

"Want a tow?" she demanded.

"I suppose so," said Jim.

I lay back and shut my eyes, ears, mind, everything.

I heard various things going on, but it did not matter. Then I felt the waves slapping against us once more. Jim sat down beside me and slapped my back.

I sank my mind a thousand miles. I tried to vanish so deep within me that I could not even feel slaps.

78

Time passed.

"The gap," I heard Jim say.

I sat up. There we were smoothing through the broad concrete channel. There was Toronto, all bright and clean, looming against the sky.

"Land ho," hailed Jim.

"Erck," said I.

Which shows that salt can be diluted right out of your blood.

Summer
Orphans

August 11, 1934

"Well," said Jimmie Frise, "what'll we do to-night?"

"Let's wash dishes," I suggested. "I have a sink full, besides another pile on the drainboard and a few on the kitchen table."

"Mine," said Jimmie, "are neatly stacked in piles in the sink. All scraped. Are yours scraped?"

"No," I admitted rather shamed. "They're just the way I put them down."

"You've been a summer bachelor often enough," criticized Jimmie, "to know better than leave dishes unscraped. All you need to do is spread out the morning paper on the kitchen table, scrape the egg, corn flakes or tomato squitters off the plates, empty the coffee cup, and pile the dishes and roll up the newspaper and toss it in the garbage pail. It's no trouble at all. Yet it saves that funny smell that pervades a man's house in the summer when his family is at the cottage."

"I know, I know," I admitted. "I have been intending to scrape my dishes for years. But somehow, a summer bachelor feels so dreary and low in his spirits, he can't even summon enough energy to do a little thing like that. I hate my bed, too. All muddled and wrinkled."

"Don't you even change your bed?" cried Jimmie.

"Oh, I sometimes do," I assured him. "But it's such a problem, pulling the old sheets out and then working the new sheets back under the blanket and quilt."

80

*We carried the dishes
upstairs, stacked them
in the bathtub and
turned on the shower.*

"You don't do that!" scornfully cried Jim. "You pull all the bedclothes off, throw them on a chair, spread fresh sheets, and then put the blankets . . ."

"But you have to have somebody on the other side of the bed," I explained. "To tuck in the far side."

"Ach!" snorted Jim disgustedly. "You a summer bachelor! Do you know what you are? You're a summer orphan."

"I get along pretty well," I protested.

"Listen," said Jim, "I'll tell you what to do to-night. If you'll help me with my dishes, I'll help you not only with your dishes but I'll help you change your bed."

"Swell," I agreed.

What to do with yourself in the evenings is one of the eternal problems of that class of men whose families go away to summer cottages. Movies are good for so long. Sunnyside is good for a couple of trips. Watering the lawn is splendid maybe for about the last two nights of the week, Thursday and Friday, when you are feeling as homesick as possible and looking forward to seeing them all on Saturday; and it gives you a strange, virtuous feeling, a sort of religious feeling, to water the grass in their honor. But watering the grass is no good Monday, Tuesday and Wednesday evenings.

"Let's eat supper downtown," suggested Jim, "and then we'll go to your place first, wash your dishes, make your bed, and then over to my place. It will fill up the evening beautifully."

For the Big Clean-Up

"Where will we eat?" I asked rather mournfully.

Jim looked thoughtful. We summer bachelors eat our way right around the city. It isn't that the restaurants are not good. They are all good. But after a few tries, each one gets on your nerves. So you try something different. You are seeking something unknown, unseen, indescribable. You are seeking your own home. But you don't know it. So you go anxiously, like a wolf in a cage, from place to place, seeking. And not finding.

Jim named one restaurant. I made a face. Then I named a restaurant. And Jim made a face. So we decided to go to my house and pick up some tomatoes, cheese and a small bottle of cream at the corner store.

The house, when we entered, had that stuffy smell, of closed doors and windows, of stale smoke, of unwashed dishes in the kitchen. Maybe two weeks' dishes.

"Phoo!" said Jim.

So we ate our tomatoes and cheese out in the garden, on the rustic table. And then we peeled up our sleeves and entered the kitchen for the big semi-monthly clean-up. As I had told Jim, my dishes were partly in the sink, partly on the drainboard, and the rest of them were laid on the table, the kitchen cabinet and the gas stove.

"Even if you piled them up," argued Jim, "it would give you some feeling of decency. Why do you scatter them around like this?"

I spread a newspaper and started to scrape. But the stuff on the dishes, odds and ends, had dried tight to the dishes and you needed a chisel, not a paring knife, for a scraper.

"Put them in the sink and soak them while we make the bed," suggested Jim.

"The sink isn't big enough," I pointed out.

"Ah," cried Jim, "An idea! Look here, why should we summer bachelors be slaves to woman's way of doing things? Let us carry these dishes up to the bathroom and do them in the bathtub!"

"There's an idea!" I shouted. "Why should we be handicapped by a silly little sink?"

"Put them in the bathtub," said Jim, "let the water run on them, leave the plug open, and the current will wash them automatically, all we have to do is come along and dry them. Come on."

So we got trays and we loaded up the dishes, plates, cups, bowls, saucers and all those things you never saw before but which you found in back of the china closet when you started to run short of dishes about the third week. Dishes, little pitchers, funny plates that you dimly remembered having seen when you were a boy.

We carried them up and stacked them in the bathtub. We turned on the shower both hot and cold, although there was no hot water, of course. But the spray of water splashed and roared on the dishes, and in a minute or two, we began to see the remnants of scrambled egg and toast crusts come loose and vanish down the hole.

"Marvellous!" yelled Jim, above the noise of the shower. "We have discovered something every summer bachelor should know."

By shifting the pile of dishes now and again, the streams of water went new ways, found new channels, and every new way they went, the streams of pure water did good.

"Let's make your bed while they wash," said Jim proudly. "It's automatic."

So we went in and Jim showed me how to haul the bedclothes off with one large swipe, fling them on a chair, and then he and I laid fresh sheets, and put back the light blanket and the quilt. Jim even tucked the quilt up that way the ladies do, you know, sort of dented in the middle with the two ends flounced out.

"Ah," I said. "I'll hate to disturb it tonight."

"I'll come and help you make it any time," said Jim grandly.

We went back into the bath tub and there the top dishes were already shining white, and we shifted the pile loosely, exposing new surfaces to the rushing water. You could see the old stuff whirling about and vanishing down the pipe.

"Look here," said Jim, "let's leave them and run over to my place and put mine in the bath tub. And by the time we get back, they will be ready to dry."

"Won't they be kind of greasy?" I asked. "We should put soap on them."

"Where's your soap flakes?" asked Jim.

I ran down cellar and got a package of soap flakes, which we sprinkled liberally over the pile, and even the cold water made foamy suds. A lot of the flakes caught in various places in the pile which would melt in time.

"Come on," said Jim.

So we walked the two blocks over to Jim's house, carried his dishes up to his bathroom, piled them and turned the water on and scattered soap flakes all over them. We also went in and saw Jim's garden for a few minutes, and

chatted with a neighbor who knew all about zinnias. And
then we strolled back to my place.

We went in the garden and sat down. Through the
open bathroom window we could hear the shower mum-
bling. Occasionally we could hear a dish clink.

"Having solved the dish problem," said Jim, leaning
back in the garden seat, "let us turn our attention to the
laundry of a summer bachelor. You know, all it takes is a
little attention to solve any kind of problem. Women are
set in their ways. They have their little dinky way of
doing things. Little sinks. Little dish towels. Everything
is tiny and routine and sissy. Now, if we men can improve on dish washing, why can't we improve on
laundry? In time to come, I would not be surprised if, instead of a little sink, and dishes to wash three times a
day, the house of the future will have a huge sink in it,
where all the dishes will be put after each meal. And
then, at night, one big dish washing bee will be held.
How much more freedom this would give to womanhood!
One dish-washing bee each day, on a large scale. It
would be a lot cheaper to buy a few more dishes than to
spend three-quarters of an hour three times every day,
like a slave, washing a few dishes. We haven't solved the
problems of the domestic world yet. Science needs to pay
attention to the home."

"It isn't science so much as just common sense, Jimmie," I said. "That bath tub idea has been staring mankind in the face ever since bath tubs were invented. Yet
who thought of it?"

"I did," said Jim, "in the year 1934. Let's remember
it."

We chatted on, philosophically.

"Perhaps I should run up and shake a few more soap
flakes over the pile," I suggested. "I don't hear the
taps."

"Maybe Women are Right"

We listened.

There was no mumble of the taps. "That's funny," said
Jim, half rising.

"Jimmie!" I gasped.

85

We had both thought of the same thing. We leaped and ran to the back door.

We were too late.

The back entrance is a French door leading directly into the dining room. When we opened the doors we were at first confused. The dining room had disappeared. The wallpaper was drooping in large glistening festoons from the ceiling. I thrust through the clinging jungle. Water was dripping merrily, briskly. Bumping against tables and chairs, I got into the hall, where there is a painted plaster ceiling. Into the front lobby I dashed to find a cascade of water pouring down the front stairs. There was a secret, busy air of water seeping, creeping, crawling, dripping, everywhere. I sloshed upstairs, Jim behind me.

"Oh, gosh!"

The bath tub was overflowing, and cups and bowls were floating happily in a little sea.

"It's plugged, Jim," I moaned. "Something plugged it."

"Toast crusts," cried Jim. "Bacon rind."

I snapped the taps off. An inch of water lay all over the floor and out into the bedrooms, the rugs were soggy, the garments I had thrown on the floor of different rooms, the items of next week's laundry that I had tossed aside on various floors, all, all were sodden. We heard strange, mysterious slithering, slickery sounds downstairs again. We hurried below, to find wallpaper slithering off walls, collapsing off ceilings. We tore it away, to discover tables, chairs, upholstery soaked and soggy. The chesterfield was like a vast pudding.

"Oh, Jimmie," I moaned.

"You'll have to excuse me," said Jim, starting for the front door. "I got to get home and turn off my shower."

"Don't leave, Jim!" I shouted. "Not now."

But Jim was gone.

I waded about for some minutes, baling, mopping, sloshing. What a terrible thing! Then the telephone rang. It was Jim.

"I got my taps in time," said he. "Come on over and help me with my dishes and let that place dry overnight.

You had better stay over here with me to-night."

"All right, Jim."

"We can see what has to be done better to-morrow at your place. Let her subside."

"All right, Jim."

"And incidentally, maybe women have the right idea about things. Maybe sinks are better for dishes."

"You're right, Jim."

So I got my hat and went over to Jim's.

Semi-Nudism

August 25, 1934

"Look at you," declared Jimmie Frise. "Almost at the end of the summer and you haven't a speck of color."

"I got a good tan in July," I said.

"It's all gone now," stated Jim. "You look as pallid as a garment worker. You have no more color than a sheep.

"We're fried," I said. "My friend here can't turn over and I don't bend anywhere but in the middle."

The summer is the time we Canadians should soak up the sun and warmth to carry us over the long and blood-chilling winter."

"I don't tan," I said. "I burn."

"Everybody tans," corrected Jim. "Some of us have to take it in easy stages, but we tan. Tan is the sign that you have done your duty, as a good Canadian, in so far as storing up energy against the winter. Like bees storing up honey."

"I guess I have it inside of me," I suggested.

"Look at those kids now," said Jim.

Two girls and two boys were walking along King St. ahead of us. The boys were both shock-headed blonds and the girls were sleek brunettes. The boys were bare-armed, bare-necked and they were tanned a gorgeous orange shade. The girls, their backs and shoulders bared by print dresses, were a deep chocolate.

"There," cried Jimmie, "are true Canadians. They will survive the winter. They will be full of pep next March when the last fatal blizzards blow."

"Jimmie," I accused, "I believe you are a nudist at heart."

"No, just a semi-nudist," said Jim. "I'm going down to Sunnyside this afternoon and lie in the sun. I think you should come along."

"It's a pretty hot day."

"This late-season sun doesn't burn," assured Jim. "It has lost its sting. The sun is already sloping far down to the south, only we don't realize it. The weather is still hot because all the heat the sun has been baking and pouring on to the earth this last two months keeps things warm. The earth has been doing what we should do. It has been soaking up the sun. But there is no kick in the sun now."

"I'll come," I said, "but I think I'll bring a parasol."

Jimmie looked at me with contempt.

"You don't deserve to be a Canadian," he snorted. "You act like a soft Californian or a Jamaican. To be a Canadian you have got to be able to take it, hot or cold."

"We will have bathing suits?" I inquired.

"Trunks only," said Jim. "I'm going to wear my trunks and a sweat-shirt in the car until I get there."

After lunch Jimmie picked me up at the house. He was handsome in bright blue trunks and a yellow sweat-shirt. I wore my striped dressing gown over my regular bathing suit. I beckoned him to come into the side drive to pick me up. With my family away, I don't want the neighbors seeing me traipsing around in a striped bath robe. Sunnyside is all right. You are lost in the picture there. But summer bachelors have to use discretion.

Spectacle of Happiness

There were thousands spread along the Sunnyside shore. Bathing, beach bathing, sun bathing, in clots and mobs and family parties, along the bright shore and the blue water, they made a spectacle of color and health and happiness.

"Now," said Jimmie, coasting along the highway, "it is illegal for us semi-nudists to parade in half a bathing suit, so we just have to hunt along the beach until we see an unfrequented spot. There are hundreds of our fellow-sunworshippers there on the beach, lying flat and out of sight. The only time the police pick you up is when you walk around in full view."

"It would look fine in the papers," I said, "in the police court news—'journalists pinched for nudism.' I can't take any chances, Jim. Not with my family. Let's drive out to the country somewhere and lie down in the middle of a ten-acre field with a hollow in it."

"The beach is the proper place," said Jim. "What would the cows think of seeing us in their field? And, anyway, it would be a far worse crime to be semi-nude in the middle of a ten-acre field in the country than semi-nude on a city beach. You don't understand the rural mind."

"I'll only tan my legs and arms," I said. "And if the cops see you I'll pretend I don't know you."

Jim parked the car. Down even with us on Sunnyside were scattered bushes and long grass and far away to the east and well off toward the west were bright crawling hordes of sun-worshippers, but in front of us were just a few scattered couples.

"This is ideal," said Jimmie. "You can't see a person lying down here."

We walked down the terraces and out across the grassy and sandy approaches. The few scattered couples paid no attention to us. I observed that several of them were exposing gleaming backs to the bright rays of the sun. The water was glassy. It was a gorgeous afternoon.

Jim chose a nice spot, well distant from any others, and we lay down on the sand. Jim skilfully peeled off his yellow sweat-shirt and I removed my dressing gown and spread it for a quilt to lie on.

"Ah," we said. And it was lovely. We chatted lazily about this and that. About the ancient peoples who worshipped the sun as the giver of life. About nudism.

"The Germans started this nudism," said Jimmie. "I think it was symbolical. They went nude to show the world how thoroughly they had been stripped by the war and the peace."

"No," I said, "there has always been nudism. It is a deep instinct in us. It harks back to the ages when we all went around nude. But of course in those days we wore a heavy hide of fur all over us. But whenever a race gets weak and worn out nature starts stirring in their blood old hankerings and ancient instincts. The Germans after the war were weak and defeated, and to bring them back to life old Mother Nature waked in them the idea of running about naked. That explains all this stuff about the old gods and Hitler trying to bring back the ancient German virtues. It is like a sick man trying to show how strong and active he is. He sticks out his chest and talks in a big deep voice, but he doesn't fool anybody."

"Mmmmmm," said Jimmie. His eyes were closed. The sun was like a flood. I looked discreetly about and as far as the eye could see was just blue water and yellow sand and couples and groups of delightful people minding their own business. And not a cop was in sight anywhere. So I slipped off the shoulder straps of my bathing suit and peeled it politely down to my waist. I lay back.

"Jimmie," I said.

"Mmmmmm," said Jimmie.

So I just lay there and drowsed and I fell asleep, too. Jimmie waked me.

"Turn over," said Jim. "You are done on the front. Now for your back."

I turned over. It felt cool and dry.

"What time is it?" I asked.

"About three-thirty," thought Jimmie. "Isn't this swell?"

"It ought to be part of the public health laws of Ontario," I declared, "to spend so many hours a week taking the sun."

So we talked on our stomachs for a while about ants and desert sand and grass and so forth. We thought of this good old earth with all the vast face of it covered by these countless, uncountable grains of sand, of all the blades of grass standing pointing at the sun in a sort of Hitler salute . . .

"Mmmmmm," said Jimmie, who has been tired of Hitler for four months.

I lay watching the ants and the small bugs and the fatheaded baby grasshoppers working out their silly destiny at the end of my nose, and the great sun fired its millions of life-giving electrons or whatever it is into my back and down my legs. I could feel them tingling rather tightly.

"Jimmie," I said quietly, "did you say the August sun had no power?"

"Mmmm," said Jim, his head on his arms.

So I fell asleep, too, and I dreamed I was Gordon Sinclair snapping my fingers under the noses of tigers in Samarkand and climbing mountains in Asia and the southern slopes, where a sun like a furnace fried my back.

Jimmie woke me.

"Wah-ho," I yawned. "Ouch!"

"It must be six o'clock," said Jim.

The sun was far over Hamilton, London and points west.

I started to roll over.

"Jimmie," I said.

"Now, now," said he. "I'm still on my face myself. Take it easy."

My back felt as if it was all bound up with court plaster. It had a cold feeling. As I lay there a kind of shiver ran across it. I tried to straighten my arms to lift my upper part clear of the sand. But my elbows would not bend.

"Jimmie, my elbows won't bend!"

"Not as bad as my knees not bending," said Jim. "Fffft! Woe is me!"

I turned my head, but something was holding the back of my neck. I moved one leg, but the skin on the back of my knee had stiffened and I had a feeling it would not stretch, like skin, but would crack, like grass.

I could see Jim. He was a bright fiery red.

"You look boiled," I gasped.

"I would sooner look boiled than fried," said he, looking me over.

I found that my middle section, covered by my bathing suit, still had a joint in it. Somehow, despite terrible lacerating sand and cruel spikey grass, I got turned over, and sat up, with arms, legs and neck held carefully rigid.

"Boy," I yelled, and even my voice felt crackly, "boy, come over here!"

A little boy was passing and came over.

"Please go and get somebody." I said, "a policeman or a fireman or a doctor. Get somebody and bring them here."

"We'll Pay For the Ambulance"

The little boy scampered away down the beach, and in a little while he returned with a great black-armed, black-chested, black-faced life-guard in a red bathing suit and a white hat.

"Well, gents," said the great mahogany life-guard.

"We're fried." I said. "My friend there can't turn over

and I don't bend anywhere but in the middle."

"Where's your car?" asked the life-guard.

"Level with us up there," groaned Jimmie.

"I'll carry you up," said he. "Once you get home you can go to bed and call the doctor."

I didn't like the thought of those great walnut hands gripping my skin. I felt as if large slithers of skin would slip off me wherever he touched me.

"Perhaps," I said, "if you could send for an ambulance with a stretcher it would be better. We'll pay for the ambulance."

"Just take it easy," said the life-guard, walking muscularly and bow-leggedly and very chocolately away.

In a few minutes he came back with two planks and a wheel-barrow.

"Easy," I begged. Jim and I were not speaking. In fact we hadn't spoken at all.

The life-guard laid the planks down beside me, rolled us on to the planks, skidded us on to the wheel-barrow and tenderly trundled us across the rolling sands and through the harsh grass and over all the ants and grasshoppers, up the terrace to our car.

"This happens all the time," he said gently. He lifted Jim in his immense black arms and I noted the contrasts between his color and Jim's. It was different.

He laid me on the back seat.

"Now," he said, "you've got a good beginning. Let this lay a couple of days and then, if you don't blister or peel, come on down for another dose. In about two weeks you'll have a nice color."

"You're very kind," Jimmie and I whispered.

Jim, like a jointed doll, slowly turned on the switch, stepped on the starter.

"I'm glad," said Jim, "there aren't many turns on the road home."

"Think of to-morrow," I said hollowly.

"What's the matter with the police force in Toronto!" demanded Jimmie, angrily, not moving his neck. "Why don't they get on the job and stop this semi-nude stuff on our beaches!"

"You're right," I said.

Pickle
Surprise
September 1, 1934

"The smell of ketchup being boiled," said Jimmie Frise, "is of all the odors in nature or art the most beautiful to me."

"It's a swell smell," I admitted.

"This season of the year," went on Jimmie, "the year in its fullness, the fields ripe, the fruits burdening the trees, everything deeply and richly colored; the sunflowers and the zinnias, the great cannas red and yellow, no pale fragile flowers left, but only the blazing hues; the season of completion, of consummation, of perfection; and over it floating like an incense of thanksgiving the smell of pickling. Especially ketchup."

"It smells swell," I confirmed.

"Spring," said Jimmie, "is like a child, beautiful, winsome and all that. But you have no desire to seize spring and hug her to your bosom. Early summer is like a young woman. Beautiful, attractive, but you can't be sure whether she is sulky or perhaps she has funny teeth or maybe a high, squeaky voice. But late summer, ah, and early fall! There's the woman, the matron, the mother of many children. Her character stands clearly before you. She smiles and is at ease, her chief work done."

"What's winter, Jim?" I asked.

"Some old dame," growled Jim, with a look at the weather. "I wish my family was home from the cottage and all of them up to their elbows in pickles. I'd stay home all day and lie on the chesterfield, with the radio going, and just inhale the pickle smell until I was saturated."

"You are all worked up," I remarked.

"It seems to purify the lungs," said Jim. "It is the deepest breath you can take, pickle smell. It touches those farthest, deepest, little corners of your lungs, like

Into the big preserving kettle we
ladled them, spices and powders,
vinegar and mustard.

97

the ears of a pillow slip that haven't been touched for ages."

"My family will be home soon," I said, "and you can come over and hang around while they are pickling."

"What do they make?" asked Jim, sitting up eagerly.

"Oh, ketchup," I said, "and a kind of chopped-up mustard pickle with a lot of celery seed and curry in it."

"Ah," breathed Jim.

"And then a kind of small gherkins," I added, "not sweet, not sour, but a kind of crisp, crunchy, sweetish, vinegary . . ."

"Stop!" cried Jim.

"Then we do up some pickled peaches," I said, "with cloves. And crabapples and pickled punkin."

"Pickled punkin?" exclaimed Jim.

"Well, some kind of squash or something," I said. "It comes out in sort of square transparent pieces about the size of a small matchbox and it is lovely with cold beef."

"Oooh!" breathed Jimmie.

"Then we make a kind of conserve," I said, "with plums, peaches, apples and a lot of spices dumped in. It is different every year. It is a sort of adventure, after all the other pickling is done and there are still a dozen and half sealers left over and some odds and ends of peanut butter jars and things."

"The Women Have All the Fun"

"Personally," said Jim, "I don't think women adventure half enough in the realm of pickles. Look at all the things there are to pickle and all the different ways there are to pickle them. In brine, in vinegar; sweet, sour; yet when all is said and done we have only four or five kinds of pickles. Look at the grocery store shelves. Not six different kinds. You would think there would be hundreds of kinds."

"I've often thought," I said, "that I might take a whirl at a little pickling myself. Some experimenting, you know. When the ladies are out some afternoon, after the regular pickling season is over."

"The women," said Jim, "have all the fun."

"It isn't hard," I pointed out. "You just get the big

preserving kettle and you boil up whatever you are doing, with either vinegar or sugar to preserve it. And you put it into the sealers, and there you are."

Jim looked at me out of the sides of his eyes.

"What do you say," he asked, "if we try to work out a pickle of our own?"

"Any time," I agreed.

"A pickle," said Jim, "that will embody all the things we like. Onions, curry, everything."

"I bet we could work out a pretty fair pickle," I concurred.

"Partly sweet," said Jim, "and partly sour. Briney at the same time. A pickle that will be all pickles at once."

"I don't see," I suggested, "why we shouldn't include ketchup in the recipe. Work ketchup right in with mustard pickles, for example. And when you are eating them you never could tell when a nice snappy whole gherkin might pop up on your plate."

"We will call it," said Jim, "pickle surprise."

"We'll make it at my house to-morrow," I said.

"No, no," begged Jimmie. "I have everything ready at my house."

"It was me suggested making them," I said. "If it is a success we can then go over to your house the next day and make you up a batch."

"It will be a success all right," assured Jim. "It isn't like baking a cake. It is all in the ingredients."

I went home early and spent the evening preparing for the pickling bee. I brought up from the cellar a good supply of sealers, quart and pint sizes, and a number of those numerous assorted jelly jars and modernistic marmalade glasses that seem to accumulate in a house nowadays.

I got the two big preserving kettles up and went through all the cupboards left so tidy during the absence of the family for the summer and laid out rows and rows of spices. There was allspice and cloves, tumeric and nutmeg, cassia and capsicum.

There was a bottle of "Preservit" and a small bottle labelled "Kitchen Kumfort, Gives a Flavor to Everything." There was even a vial of bright red coloring and

99

on it it said "Preserving."

There was celery salt and paprika, onion salt and bay leaves.

Jimmie and I started by calling at the corner store for the raw materials of our pickle surprise. We got gherkins and silver onions, cauliflower and tomatoes.

"And why not a cabbage?" asked Jim. "If cauliflower, why not cabbage?"

So we took the cabbage. And beets and string beans and two quarts of vinegar and a large tin of mustard.

And, laden with baskets and bags, we repaired to my house for the great experiment. We laid out all the materials and stripped to our BVD's like sailors going into action.

Trusting to Inspiration

"Now," said Jim, "what is to be the foundation of this pickle?"

"Gherkins," said I.

"Ketchup," disagreed Jim. "Ketchup will be the liquid in which all the rest of the things float."

"Very well," I said, "we will peel the tomatoes first and boil them and strain them through a cloth bag or a fresh sock."

"That's a woman's way of doing it," said Jimmie. "This is to be a man's pickle. We'll just dump the tomatoes in like everything else."

"But the skins will come loose," I expostulated. "And go floating around like pieces of chamois or those exploded toy balloons."

"As we stir the pickle," said Jim, "we can catch the skins as they appear, then fork them out."

"How much water do you put in the kettle to start with?" I asked.

"About three or four inches," said Jim.

"Should we wash the cauliflower and things?" I asked.

"Nonsense," said Jim. "Modern public health laws have done away with all those old-fashioned things. Vegetables and fruits nowadays are sanitary before they go before the public."

"We just dump them in?"

"Correct," said Jim. "Only we can cut them up into loose pieces."

So we cut up tomatoes and cauliflower, cabbage and beets, string beans and celery. The gherkins and little silver onions we left whole.

"The gherkins feel a bit gritty," I offered.

"That's just the natural feel of them," said Jim. "How much salt?"

"Oh, a handful or two," said I.

We turned on the stove before starting to mix the spices and flavourings. Then we went to the kitchen cabinet shelf and selected the spices.

"Allspice," read Jim. "A couple of good handfuls."

"Tumeric," said I. "A level spoonful or two."

Into the big preserving kettle we ladled them, spices and powders, Kitchen Kumfort and Preservit, vinegar and mustard.

"How about this coloring?" asked Jim, examining the little bottle.

"It's for coloring jellies and cakes," I explained.

"Most pickles are a dull brown or greenish gray," said Jim. "Pickle surprise will be noted for its bright, happy color. Like cranberry jelly on the New Year's dinner table."

He dumped in the contents of the bottle.

"What's this?" asked Jim.

"Beef cubes," I replied.

"H'm," said Jim, peeling one and tossing it into the pot.

"Now," said he, "when it begins to cook, we can taste it from time to time and add this and that to get it right. The way women go by the rules is the reason all pickles are alike. We will trust to inspiration."

To let it get started we went in and turned on the radio, one or the other of us going into the kitchen every few minutes to see if it was boiling.

It took a long time to get going. But once it did, the most exciting odors began to fill the house. We stirred the cauldron, which had not yet taken on any definite color, but was red and green and white and yellow as the various ingredients floated to the surface. But the red coloring extract and the tomatoes were slowly exerting themselves and the faster it boiled the redder it got.

"Let's walk over to the store and see if there is anything we have overlooked," suggested Jimmie. "It will take a long time for those cauliflowers and onions to cook. Don't let's spoil it by hurrying."

Over at the store we got some radishes and an egg plant.

"There are two things I never heard of being pickled," said Jim.

The man in the store suggested that plums and peaches made an awfully nice base for a mixed pickle. So we took some fruit and Jim got a small box of preserved ginger.

"It's a sort of spice," he explained.

Everything But Spinach

When we got home we split the big kettle's contents in half and filled both the cauldrons, adding the new things we had bought. I caught Jimmie slipping a banana into the kettle.

"Who ever heard of a pickled banana?" I demanded.

"That's the point," said Jimmie.

So the two cauldrons stewed and boiled and everything began to cook and get soft, and the rich red color began to dominate. Such softish items as the banana and the cauliflower gradually collapsed and grew limp and dissolved themselves amidst the multitude, while the firmer items, such as the cucumbers, got rather swollen and pale looking. The radishes bobbed about the top and the tomato skins swirled up and Jimmie and I were kept busy watching for them and snatching them as they were flung upward in the boiling. And the richest spicy odor imaginable filled the house.

"We ought to start tasting now," said Jim. So we took spoons and blew and cooled and tasted.

"M'm," said I. "It doesn't taste like anything."

"That," said Jim, "is because it tastes like everything."

But I could not detect it.

"It needs a little more character," I suggested, "and it ought to be thicker. It is too loose the way it is. I hate loose pickles."

"Ketchup is loose," pointed out Jimmie.

Yet it didn't taste like ketchup and it didn't taste like mustard pickles and it didn't taste like gherkins. It had a taste all its own.

"A kind of surprising taste," said Jim. "That is why we call it pickle surprise."

"I think it has stewed long enough," I said. "How would you like to rinse off those sealers?"

Jim turned the tap on and rinsed the sealers while I got the ladle and prepared to scoop the surprise into the bottles. Jim put them on a tray as he rinsed them and I ladled in the pickle.

"Snick!" went the first jar.

"Snuck!" went the second jar.

"Tinkle, click," went the third one.

"Those jars are cracking!" cried Jimmie.

So we waited for the pickle to cool before putting it in the jars, which we since have been told is not good practice.

We went to supper and came back and tasted the cooling pickle surprise.

It was gritty.

I mean, in addition to everything else, it was gritty.

"You should have washed those beets," I complained to Jim. "And the cauliflower. In fact, we should have washed everything."

"That reminds me," said Jim, rinsing out his mouth at the sink. "We forgot spinach. In our next batch we must put in some spinach."

"And a parsnip or two," I said. "When we do your batch we can profit by what we learned with this."

But at bedtime Jim telephoned to say his family had arrived home from the cottage.

"They will be making ketchup Friday," he said. "How about coming over for the afternoon?"

"Swell," said I.

So I gave my seven bottles and four jars to charity.

An Old Lady's Hat

September 22, 1934

I drew forth the yellow 20 dollar bill and casually handed it to him without even looking at it or him.

"Do you know," asked Jimmie Frise, "who are the happiest people in the world to-day?"

"The Eskimos?" I ventured.

"No," said Jimmie, "the bums. The fellows who ask you for a dime. They're the happiest. Not a care in the world. And always guaranteed, by the eternal goodness of human nature, a dime."

"That's very interesting," I said. "You think human nature can always be depended upon to the extent of a dime?"

"Yes," said Jimmie. "That is the measure of it. If it were more, bums would ask for more. It is the ancient and exact measure. You never hear a bum ask for fifty cents or a dollar. That is, except some of the bums that are your personal friends."

"I wonder what a bum would do," I asked "if you did give him a dollar? Or ten dollars!"

"Or twenty," said Jimmie. "Imagine walking along the street and a bum shambles up beside you and asks for a dime and you nonchalantly reach into your pocket and hand him a twenty dollar bill. What would he do?"

"Probably drop dead from heart failure," I guessed.

"No, now, there's an interesting experiment," went on Jim. "We could go out on the street, and you walk a few paces ahead of me and be the one the bum would ask. You hand him the twenty and I'll follow him. We'll just see what a bum would do with a lot of money."

"He would head for the first beer joint," I said.

"I don't know," demurred Jimmie. "Maybe he would head for the barber shop and then go and get a new suit. It would be interesting to find out."

"We would have the pleasure," I said, "of seeing our hard earned twenty being shot to pieces in record time on a lavish investment in rubbing alcohol, native wine and canned heat. I can think of better investments."

"You have a very poor opinion of your lesser brethren," said Jim. "I find it convenient to believe that a heart of gold beats beneath those shabby outer integuments. Just give the boys a chance, and they will rise, not fall. Anyway, it would be very interesting just to see what would happen if we handed out, to the first bum we met, not a selected bum but just any old bum, a twenty dollar bill. How about contributing ten of it?"

"Who is going to hand the money out?" I questioned.

"You could," said Jim, generously.

"Very well," I said, because it wouldn't be the first time I had been manipulated into paying the entire cost of one of our social experiments.

"I tell you," suggested Jimmie, "we'll make a little gamble of it. If the bum does what I think he will do, that is, buy some clothes or pay his room rent, you pay $15 of the cost of the experiment. If he heads for the beer joint, or otherwise flings the money away, I'll pay $15 of the $20. How about it?"

"Now it's a sporting proposition," I agreed. "I like to see optimists pay 75 per cent of the costs."

The Happiest People

"I said," pointed out Jimmie, "that the bums were the happiest people in the world, because they had no cares. Did you ever read Thoreau's 'Walden'?"

"Not yet," I admitted.

"Well, it's a book nearly a hundred years old that ought to be a best seller to-day," said Jim. "It answers all the questions people are asking these times. In it, Thoreau shows that every bit of property you acquire, whether it is only a rake or a hoe, or block of a quarter

106

million shares of stock, is tied around your neck like a stone. And the more you possess, the more hopelessly are you burdened."

"I don't mind a few burdens," I said.

"These bums," said Jim, "are secure in their belief that somebody, every day, is sure to be found good enough at heart to save them from starving. What more do they want?"

"I suppose they have a lovely free feeling," I said. "With us, it isn't a question of where is the next meal coming from. It is the question, where are the meals we have had for the past two or three years coming from?"

"Now you've hit it," said Jim. "And I want to see the face of the guy you give that $20 to."

We changed our various small bills into one $20. We arranged that I would stroll along the street in an expansive and leisurely manner, looking as much like a stockholder as possible, while Jim would come ten or fifteen paces in rear of me so that the bum would not notice him. I have the faculty of being able to disguise myself completely with nothing more than my hat. If I wear my hat in the middle of my head and perfectly straight, I look like the organist in a Methodist Sunday school. If I wear it where it feels most natural, on the side, I look like the proprietor of a pool room. I was to wear my fall coat until I had given the $20, and carry the coat thereafter. A fall coat carried over the arm gives a man a very racy look.

We went out to King St. We walked to Yonge. No bums. It was around 3 p.m., which is a good time for bums. We turned up Yonge and worked back to the office district via Adelaide. Up Bay again and west on Richmond St. Reflected in shop windows, I could see Jimmie following me casually along.

Then we met our bum. He was walking slowly toward me. He was the typical panhandler. Coat and pants did not match. Shoes pretty soft looking. Panhandlers, like all other kinds of people about to commit some irregularity, never know what to do with their hands. They usually hold them together in front of them, twisting the fingers. I suppose it is because a panhandler doesn't want to accost you with his hands in his pockets for fear

107

you would be frightened. He shows his hands, a mute, unconscious gesture of his humility and innocence.

As this bum selected me for the touch, he turned quickly and started walking the same way I was walking, only slower, so that I would catch up to him.

As I came level with him, he cast a quick, furtive look around, and then sidled alongside of me.

"Say," he said, confidentially, "could you spare the price of a cuppa coffee, mister . . ."

Keeping right on walking, but bending my head sympathetically, I said:

"Why, sure," and reached into my pocket. After a moment's pause as I felt about in my pocket the usual way, I drew forth the rich yellow $20 and casually handed it to him, without even looking at it or him.

For an appreciable moment, he just kept walking beside me, and I could see he was looking down at my hand.

"Here you are," I said, shortly, speeding up a little, and thrusting the bill at his dangling hand. He took it. I walked straight on.

Panhandler Goes Shopping

Jim had paused and was looking in a window. I went on a few doors, as prearranged, and then stepped into the lobby of what happened to be an office furniture store where I studied the hat racks and roll top desks, watching out the big window.

Jim says the man stood like a statue, head bent, hand in pocket, where he had whisked the bill. For a long moment after I had disappeared, he stood there. Then he raised his head slowly, and looked all around, at the street, at the passerby, at the windows above.

Very slowly he turned and with dragging feet, he walked back past Jimmie, staring at the pavement with a stunned look, his face brightly flushed.

I waited a full minute in the furniture store before walking casually out onto the street again. There, almost out of sight was Jimmie, anxiously looking back. I snatched off my rain coat, tipped my hat to its proper angle, and chased along until I caught up with Jimmie in the southwest entrance of a big department store.

"Hurry," said Jim, "we'll lose him in here!"

But we didn't. There he was ahead of us, slowly advancing, as if he were timid, into the resplendent aisles of the big store. Carefully, by circling around aisles and counters, we followed him, filling in the pauses, as he stopped and stared at the various displays.

"I win," said Jim. "He's going to buy new clothes!"

I had my first good look at him now. He looked stunned. Every few seconds a kind of shy grin would start to spread over his face, and he would chase it with a frightened glance around. One hand was tightly in his pants pocket.

"He's afraid to offer the $20," said Jim.

He looked at the men's clothing, the cameras, the school text books. He wandered down the long bright aisle where they have all the little islands filled with lingerie, beads, gloves. When he stopped at the bead counter and fingered a string of pink beads, the girl looked at him more in surprise than anger, and he hastily dropped the 20-cent string of beads and went on down the aisle. He came to the escalator and asked the uniformed girl a question. She motioned him up the escalator and followed him with her eyes filled with a cold amusement.

"Pardon me," I said to the girl, "would you please tell us what that bum wanted to find?"

"Ladies' hats," she laughed. "Old ladies' hats."

"It's gone to his head," I suggested to Jimmie as we trailed him up the escalator.

Among the counters and the racks and knobs of the ladies' hat department he wandered, timidly pausing and looking side-ways at certain hats, always moving away when a clerk came near. Then a short, stout lady with gray hair popped up to him and they went back to where there were some elderly ladies' hats—you know the kind.

He bought a black one, with a purple ribbon across it. He handed his $20 bill out quickly, without looking at it. The saleslady took it unconcernedly, and after a pause brought him the change, and the hat done up in one of

109

those paper hat bags of a bright brown color. Before we had time to question the saleslady, he was speeding for the escalator and we had to follow.

We followed him out into the street, along Queen to Church. Never a moment did he pause, across against the red lights he went, with shabby legs striding strongly. With one hand tight in his pants pocket.

Our Lesser Brethren

A way beyond Church he went, until we came to those streets where dwell our lesser brethren.

Up one of them he hastened, and into a tall gray house in whose windows hung the cracked card, "Bed 25c." Across that grassless hand-breadth of lawn, into that shabby door he went.

"So what?" I said.

"Of all things, an old lady's hat," said Jim.

We went to the corner and stood there. We walked to the other end of the block and stood there, debating, questioning. Nearly half an hour went by.

"We could go to the house," argued Jim, "and say we were sanitary inspectors or something. Or we were thinking of buying it. That's it, the real estate men had sent us."

We went back and rapped, since there was no bell. A girl of fourteen or so, dirty and small, answered.

"Is your momma in?"

"No, she's working."

"Your poppa?"

"He's out."

"Well, now, that's too bad. The real estate man said we could come and look through the house, we were thinking of buying it. It's for sale, isn't it?"

"I wouldn't know," said the little girl. "We just board here."

"Well, do you think it would be all right if we just walked through the house to get an idea of what it is like?" asked Jim.

"I guess so. It's a nice house. It's the best one we have ever stayed in," said the little girl proudly." The bath is

110

of marble."

"Well, now," exclaimed Jimmie.

Into the high dark hall we stepped. There was no dining room. The dining was a family apartment. Terrible tangled kitchen, with an empty high-chair standing there, and a holy picture on the wall. Up the steep, old fashioned stairs we went, the little girl showing us the rooms, rapping for us and explaining to the strange stern women and men who answered the knock, that we were gentlemen sent by the real estate. She showed us the marble bath. Oh, isles of Greece, where burning Sappho . . .

But none of the knocks revealed our man.

"Are there more rooms?" asked Jim.

"In the attic," said the little girl. "But the old lady is sick there."

"If you don't mind" said Jim. "We can just take a peep."

He was there. In the front attic room, with its steep ceiling. He was sitting on a chair drawn up close by the bed.

The bed had a patch quilt worked in two colors of gray. Light gray and dark gray. And in the bed sat against the soiled pillow, a very old and a very thin woman. I am sorry she was not beautiful and pale in a lovely way, but her white hair hung in straight wisps down about her sunken face.

On her lap lay a new black hat with a purple ribbon.

"Pardon me," said Jimmie, stepping right in. "We were sent by the real estate people. We are thinking of buying. Do you mind, please?"

"Go ahead," said the bum, shifting his chair. He had to let go the two hands of the old lady. They were like bones.

We walked about the little room with its bed, its unmatched dresser, its two chairs and its terrible bits of this and that flung about. We stalled for time looked at the window sills and frames, all in a silence as thick as soup.

As we turned away, our inspection ended, Jim said, gently:

"Not very well, eh?"

"I'm all right now," said the old lady in a husky voice. "My boy has got a job!"

The man turned a surly face to glance at us, and in that instant, he recognized me. His face went white and he continued to stare at me with a frozen expression. I tried to signal back to him with my eyes.

Everybody Has Cares

"Yes," said the old lady, "my boy. He's got a job. And what's more, his new boss gave him $20 in advance. You see, we are not on relief."

"Why not?" demanded Jim. "My goodness."

"Well, you see, we came here . . ."

"I got into trouble with the pol . . ."

"Now, now, Jimmie," said the old lady, laying her hand on the bum's arm. "For reasons we have of our own, we came to Toronto from where we had lived for years, and we haven't been here long enough to be on relief."

"Well, I hope you'll soon be well now," said Jim.

"Ah, well," sighed the old lady.

We went out and down the attic stairs, and the bum followed us, after closing the door. He came right down to the ground floor and on to the street where he touched my arm.

"Aren't you the gentleman?"

"Yes," I said.

"It was like this," said the bum. "I was brought up good as a boy. So I was walking along that street, and I was praying to God. And I said: 'God, please let me do something good for her just once before she goes.' She's going to die any day, mister. It's one of those terrible things, you know."

"Sure," I said, because it is so easy to say.

"I said to God, just let me get her some little things, a nice room where she could look out the window. Or maybe a dress. It would be only about three dollars, God, for a week for a good room. And then I touched you, mister, and you gave me that twenty."

"That's all right, that's all right," I assured him.

112

"I've been a tough egg," said the bum. "I just wanted to do one good thing. I even thought of boots for her, mister. Wasn't that funny?"

"Yes," I said.

"Boots," said the bum. "But, anyway, when you handed me that twenty, mister, I thought I would drop dead right there. It was like I saw an angel. It was like something you didn't believe and it happened."

"I am sorry," I said.

"Did you want it back?" asked the man, and I noticed for the first time he needed a shave and that he had a poor weak mouth.

"Certainly not," I said. "This is just a coincidence. I am in the real estate business."

"I see," said the bum, but he couldn't see.

"Good-by," I said.

"Thank you, mister," he said, but it was not me he was thanking, I could see that. He was still in a daze from having seen brighter glories from those low mountain tops on which the poor may stand.

Jim and I went straight down to King St. and slowly back. I think we both wanted to talk but we had cramps in our throats.

However, there is a little second-hand store window away along east there where they have old bayonets and mugs with "Down She Goes", painted on them and views of early Toronto. We always look in that window. It pulled us together.

"You see," said Jim. "That proves that we are wrong when we think there are some fortunate people, like bums or millionaires, who haven't a care in the world. I guess everybody has cares."

"You can't tell," I said, "where a dime is going when you give it away."

"By the way," said Jim, "you pay $15."

"Not on your life," I assured him. "You said he would buy clothes for himself and get a shave."

"You said he'd get pie-eyed," countered Jim.

"I guess it's fifty-fifty," said I.

"Fair enough," agreed Jim, glad to be back on the solid ground again where all happy-go-lucky people dwell.

113

Wiener

"The trouble," said Jimmie Frise, "with everything to-day is that us parents don't take enough interest in our children."

"Oh, I don't know," I said. "When I was a kid they used to sell a thing called a grab bag down at the candy store. It cost one cent. And we were lucky if we got one cent a week with which to buy one grab bag."

"I don't refer to how generous we are with our children," said Jim.

"Kids never had so much as they have nowadays," I put in. "Toys, bicycles, ice cream cones every day, nickels, dimes, quarters. They can go to movies. They can sit up special nights to hear programs. I don't think children ever had such generosity and freedom showered upon them. If children had any decency about them they should respond to our generosity by being the most perfect children of all time."

"Like everybody else," said Jimmie, "you are working up an excuse for your own delinquency. The reason you are generous to your children is to be rid of them. Instead of devoting an hour or two to them you buy them off, you get them things to play with, you fling them money to be rid of them, send them to movies, let them be entertained by a radio program to escape the duty of entertaining them yourself."

"Jimmie," I said indignantly.

"Think it over," continued Jim. "It isn't generosity that prompts you to give your children such freedom and such generous gifts. It is just to be rid of them."

"That's a shocking accusation," I declared.

"It applies to more than seventy-five percent of parents to-day," stated Jim. "In former times parents looked upon it as their first duty to give time and attention to their children. Our grandfathers believed that children wouldn't grow up at all unless they were tended and nurtured, like plants in a garden. So much time a day had to be spent in the garden of childhood and youth, hoeing out the weeds that had sprung up overnight,

114

are Boiled

"Maybe we are in the wrong place after all," I said.

loosening the soil about them so that their little minds could take root, and seeing that the proper nourishment of sunlight and air was free to get at the little seedlings."

"You distress me, Jimmie," I assured him.

"Little wonder," moralized Jim in a solemn voice, "that the world is full of weeds to-day."

"But what should we do?" I cried. "Children won't be bothered with us any more. They've got away from us. Can you imagine a child wanting to sit in the garden and listen to his poppa discoursing when he might be down at the neighborhood theatre seeing Buck Rogers or whatever it is?"

"You don't weed the garden with discourse," said Jim. "You use a hoe."

"Somehow I can't imagine hoeing my children," I said.

Something For the Kids

"What I mean is, we should work with and for our children, do personal things for them, show them we are personally and really interested in them and their affairs."

"For example?" I said.

"For example," said Jimmie, thinking, "the kids around my place are all talking about a wiener roast. They are all trying to collect a quarter toward the purchase of wieners, buns and mustard so as to go out some night to the Humber banks and hold a wiener roast. Now all us parents will gladly fork over the quarter each. But suppose I said to the kids, 'Look here, you folks just go ahead and gather at the meeting place. Get the fire lighted if you like. I will provide the wieners, the buns, the mustard and the marshmallows. I'll attend to boiling the wieners and all that. Let me provide the wiener roast.' What would be the effect of that?"

"It would be wonderful," I exclaimed.

"I don't know," mused Jim. "Maybe they would think I was just being nosey and trying to find out what they were doing."

"Never, Jimmie!"

"Or maybe they would think I was just a silly old guy trying to horn in on the young people's fun."

"I don't believe they would think of any such thing," I declared. "If you would let me share the thing with you I think it would be a wonderful start. We could commence doing our duty by the youth of to-day. Let us see the effect of parental interest on these young folks."

"I'll see," said Jim.

So a couple of nights ago Jim telephoned me to run over to his place, and out front was a gathering of girls and boys, high school sort of kids they were. Jimmie had broached the subject to them and they were all standing about, eagerly discussing the thing. The girls were the noisiest and the liveliest; the boys, taller than boys used to be in my day, tall and bold-eyed and not fussy about their clothes, just leaned about looking amused.

"I've just been telling the kids," said Jim, "that you and I would be delighted to provide a wiener roast for them."

"How would that appeal to you, children?" I asked.

"Swell," they said, "okay, jake, lovely, swell."

And several of them held whispered conversations between themselves, which I thought was different from my day. But they discussed plans, the place for the wiener roast, how they would get there.

"Oh, I can take a half-dozen of you in my car," I assured them.

"We got lots of cars," said the tallest boy, who had a yellow sweater on, with his braces on the outside.

"In that case," I said.

"You and I can go in the one car with the pots and pans, wieners and buns," said Jim.

"Okay," I said, "swell."

A Map of the Spot

It makes you feel good to mingle with youth, I thought. It makes you even talk like youth. You find your feet skipping up steps in a way you haven't done for years and you suddenly feel inclined to hold your stomach in and stick out your chest.

"This paying attention to the younger generation," I

117

assured Jim, as we went in to his house to look up the necessary pots and boilers, "will work both ways. It will make us feel younger. I feel sort of jaunty already."

"The youngest elderly people in the world," said Jim, "are those who have always mixed with their children."

We got out about half a dozen big kettles and boilers; we dug out long forks and spoons.

"At a wiener roast," explained Jim, "you boil the wieners."

Before supper we laid in a supply of six dozen wieners, six dozen buns, two big jars of mustard, a couple of big tins of marshmallows and a few sundries like some snappy pickles and a couple of baskets of grapes.

"Let's do it up in style," I said to Jimmie. "Something these kids will remember."

After supper I was over at Jim's, in good time to see three or four carloads of sweatered and breeked youth, piled densely in open and closed vehicles, tear away off up the street while Jim and I were loading in the provisions.

"The whole neighborhood is coming," said Jim, gleefully. "We will let them get there first and light a big fire and gather a lot of wood."

"Where are we to meet?" I asked.

"I have a map of the exact spot, the boys drew it for me," said Jim. "On the Humber north of the Malton Rd."

"Jake," said I, "swell."

And with considerable excitement and not a little anticipation, Jimmie and I set forth in the crisp dark starlight, with our load of fun and frolic for the young people.

We drove out to Weston and on to the Malton Rd. and, with the map drawn by the tall young chap in the yellow sweater with his braces on the outside, I directed Jim up the side roads and we came to the bridge, as marked, and to the dry stream bed, as marked, and to the old house and all, and we turned in the gate with the name painted on the tin mail box as marked.

"This is the right spot," I assured Jim.

Because no leaping fire, with silhouettes of youth

dancing around us, was to be seen.

"I guess they are gathering wood," said Jim.

We got out of the car and hunted about in the field and abandoned orchard shown on the map. But there were no cars parked and in the still night we could hear no voices in the distance, laughing voices of the wood gatherers.

"I guess they're not here yet," said Jim. "We can set the stuff out here and get the fire started for them."

Jim and I gathered wood in the dark and got the fire started. We had brought two milk cans full of water and we filled our kettles and got them on the bonfire. We spread out the wieners and started splitting the buns. I had thought a lot of nice little high school girls and boys would have helped with this work.

"Maybe they are waiting to let us get things ready," I suggested.

We got buns split, and on some long planks we salvaged around the bridge we made tables and laid out rows of wiener buns in readiness for the hot wieners.

The water took a long time to boil. Jim and I took turns at walking out to the road and staring both ways for lights. A dozen cars went by, but none were ours. It must have been an hour before the first bubbles began to appear in the wiener cauldrons and still no party of bright youth.

"I wonder if we should start to boil the wieners," asked Jimmie, "before they get here?"

"Maybe we are in the wrong place after all," I said.

"No, three or four of the boys helped draw that map," stated Jim, "and we have it right, even to the bridge and the gate and the name on the old tin mail box."

So we sat staring at the bonfire and thinking about the ways of the young.

"There must be some mistake," I said. "That crowd is sitting around a big bonfire somewhere near here, waiting for us. A fine disappointment this will be if we don't turn up."

"I wonder," said Jim.

So we packed the buns and the wieners back in their cartons and put the fire out with sand.

119

"We can drive around," said Jim, "until we see their fire."

We drove down to the Malton Rd. and back up three or four other side roads. With joy and expectation we saw three wiener roast fires, but with heavy hearts we found that each was surrounded by a gay and hearty crowd, but not ours.

We waited at highway crossroads, with our inside lights burning so that passing cars might recognize us if they wished to.

We saw glares in the sky and pursued them, only to find they were will o' the wisps or else Toronto. We revisited the scene of our first bonfire three times before ten o'clock, but all was darkness and silence.

"Jimmie," I said, "I wonder if those young people are just giving us the runaround?"

"Young people love wieners," said Jim, glancing back at the load of food and kettles in the back of our car.

"But they love independence more," I suggested. "Perhaps they prefer their own cooking."

"One last look," said Jim. "We don't want to come landing home with a truckload of cold raw wieners."

Up toward Woodbridge we went, following back roads and dirt roads, zig-zagging, expecting any minute to round a bend and see the welcome light of the fires of youth.

Down along the river we drove, in low gear, toiling and crawling.

"Ha," cried Jim, "this looks something like it."

Half a dozen small dim fires were burning in a flat beside the river. A steep stoney road led down, and we took it, opening gates as we progressed.

And What's the Answer

Into the flats we rolled and saw about the little fires the shadowy figures of people squatting in groups.

Our headlights caught the first cluster.

"Hoboes," said Jim. "It's a jungle. A hobo jungle."

The hoboes, young and middle-aged, lean and hard looking, rose to meet us, respectfully. Maybe they thought we were a police visit.

"Have you seen anything of a party of young people around here for a wiener roast?" I called out in the brave voice you use with hoboes.

"Not yet," they replied. From the other fires figures began strolling over to us.

"Well," said Jimmie, "it's going on for eleven o'clock and we have lost our party. We got a load of wieners and buns here and we don't want to waste them. How would they go with you?"

"Swell, jake, okay, swell," chorused the hoboes, mainly the language of youth. Or is it?

We climbed out and helped carry the cartons and cans and marshmallows and mustard and grapes across to the little fires.

Soon the little fires were dancing higher and higher. Soon twenty hungry hoboes were gathered in intense interest and astonishment, as the pots were filled with water and the succulent wieners were plopped in and the buns laid out along a plank again.

It was a festive, a gay night, and some were shaven and some were whiskered, some clean and some dirty, some young and stringy, some old and pouchy, but there in the red light of the fires were twenty happy, carefree children at a wiener roast.

"I like this better than the one we planned," I assured Jim.

But Jim was showing the hoboes how to cut wands to sharpen for toasting marshmallows, and with thick fingers the bums were delicately picking up the soft marshmallows and looking at them doubtfully.

And to songs that were not musical and voices that were husky and amidst faces that were not beautiful and bodies that were unkempt and careless, the wieners came out of the kettles and were popped into buns, and the mustard flowed, and the grapes were gobbled and the pickles were crunched, and they all bid us farewell up the hilly, stoney road, with musical honors, to wit, "For they are jolly good fellows."

"And the moral of this?" I asked Jim, as our wheels caught the smooth highway and bit into the air.

"That the world," said Jimmie, "is in a funny fix."

121

Hay! Hay!

October 6, 1934

"What you need," said Jimmie Frise, "is a sickle. You can't be going around like this cutting clover with a pair of scissors for the rest of your life."

Jim was out with me cutting clover for my guinea-pigs.

"Where would I get a sickle?" I asked.

"You know some farmers, don't you?" retorted Jim.

"Not near home," I said. "I guess I can keep up with

these guinea-pigs with the scissors if they don't multiply too fast."

"They haven't begun to multiply yet," said Jim. "If I were you I'd get a sickle or maybe a mower."

"I could write my relatives on the farm," I supposed.

"Better still," cried Jim, "we could go to one of those farm auction sales. Have you ever been to a country auction sale?"

"No," I admitted.

"Then," said Jim, "you don't know anything about human nature. You haven't even got the first letters of the alphabet of human nature. At a country auction you see mankind revealed. Stripped to the bare bones. There you see the secret of all human character exposed."

"Are they greedy?" I asked.

"Greedy nothing," said Jim. "Everybody goes to a country auction, first, to get something they want that they know the other poor fellow had. Second, to see the family secrets. Third, because an auction is one of the most entertaining country amusements."

"I'd love to go," I said.

"And you could get a sickle," said Jim. "Every farmer has a disused sickle stuck up in the barn somewhere, behind a post."

"Maybe we could pick up some other interesting objects," I said. "Early Ontario furniture, walnut highboys, old walnut tables maybe."

"Birdseye maple," corrected Jim.

"Dear me, Jimmie."

"Yes, a clerk in a store who does nothing all his life but hand out stuff with the prices marked right on it across a counter lives in a much nicer home than a farmer who tills a hundred acres of land and milks thirty cows."

"It's a wonder anybody farms," I said.

"I don't understand it myself," said Jim. "But you will get a glimmering of it when you attend an auction."

Everything Sold As Is

Jimmie did some telephoning out amongst his Birdseye Center friends and found that there was to be a sale of the farm implements, livestock and household goods of a gentleman who had died and whose widow was moving into Birdseye Center to live with her daughter.

It was called for 2 p.m. of the 20th at the late home of the deceased, second line, Birdseye township.

Jimmie and I drove out and got there just before 2 p.m. and found the road and the lane and the orchard in front of the house filled with cars, buggies and plain wagons. In groups outside the house, the men were gathered, some old men sitting on the veranda without much to say but all wearing a sort of "I told you so" expression, leaning back in their chairs and chewing imaginary nuts.

Through the windows I could see a number of ladies, with their hats on, sitting about. What is most astonishing about a country auction is that everybody is sitting around without talking. Maybe every five minutes somebody will say something. But the proper attitude at an auction is silence.

"We are just in time," I said as Jim and I parked and walked up the lane to the house.

"Better than that," said Jim.

Because it was a quarter to three when, from inside the house, appeared a stout gentleman in a cutaway coat, a bowler hat and a bulging moustache. Behind him came an important looking younger man, rather fat, who had a small rickety table and some documents.

"Ladies and gentlemen, ladies and gentlemen," cried the auctioneer in the bowler hat. I noticed he had large, protruding, dark eyes filled with a lowering anger like a bull's.

At the far side of the orchard were laid out a great variety of objects, implements, wagons, strange and useless looking things, sets of harness hung in apple trees, odd lots of rusty objects in separate heaps.

The auctioneer moved over to the neighborhood of this array, and his clerk set the table down and took a chair.

"Ladies and gentlemen," bellowed the auctioneer, rolling his eyes like a preacher quoting poetry, "we shall first dispose of the livestock. Listed before me, I see many splendid animals, ladies and gentlemen, the faithful horse, the contented cow, the timid sheep. I see listed before me, ladies and gentlemen, swine and fowls. I shall take them in the order in which they are set out on the bill. In view of the fact that there is a large and valuable quantity of new and beautiful articles, both for the comfort of the home and the efficient management of the farm, to be disposed of to-day, before I proceed to-morrow to the sale of the late Mrs. Tomkin's relics, I trust that bidding will be lively and spontaneous. You cannot go wrong here to-day, ladies and gentlemen. The late brother was, as you all know, a man of great thrift and a cautious buyer."

Everybody in the crowd looked at everybody else.

"Therefore, while everything is sold as is, you may be sure," enunciated the auctioneer, "you may be sure, ladies and gentlemen, I repeat, that you will be doing the wise thing in purchasing any of the effects of the late brother. Now, ladies and gentlemen, we shall proceed to the bill I see before me. We shall take the first item. One team of bays, sound in wind and limb and free of vice. One team of bays!"

Upon which bellow a sheepish young man came from behind the house leading a pair of horses as shy and embarrassed as a couple of Circassian slave maidens being set upon the block in ancient Rome.

"Watch That Hypnotist!"

They had been combed and curried and somebody had even painted their hoofs with a shiny oil. They nipped at each other and the young man leading them kept shaking their bridles to make them hold up their heads and pay attention.

"Look at that," cried the auctioneer, "as fine a matched team of bays as ever I saw in this county. Or in the adjacent counties for that matter. I am reliably informed that they are as beautifully matched a plow team as ever tilled the soil of Birdseye township. Am I right?"

The crowd shifted to the other foot.

"Now, ladies and gentlemen," bulged the auctioneer, with that high note a bull can get into his voice when he

125

wants to speak across three farms, "who will open the bidding on this beautiful team, sound in wind and limb, and believed to be under ten years of age?"

"Ten dollars," said a voice from over at the corner of the orchard.

The auctioneer set his bowler back and bulged at the voice.

"Ten dollars am I offered for this magnificent matched team of bays, good for ten years of sturdy, strong, powerful, willing, surging, seething service!"

"Fifteen dollars," said another voice, to relieve the tension and change the subject.

"Eighteen. Twenty. Twenty-five. Twenty-five, twenty-five. Surely, ladies and gentlemen, there is somebody in this crowd that knows horses better than that. Surely, ladies and gentlemen. Thirty. I have thirty. Who'll give me thirty-five? Thirty-five for the team, ladies and gentlemen, forty, forty, who'll give forty-five?"

And after a deal of shouting and bulging and addressing a far larger crowd than we were, addressing unseen throngs far back toward the barn and far out over a field where some ragged stooks of corn leaned lonely in the afternoon, the rolling-eyed auctioneer got it up to fifty dollars and suddenly banged his hammer and said, "Sold to the gentleman with the bent nose."

And the horses were led away and two more horses were brought out.

"How long will it take to get to the sickles?" I asked Jim.

"Take your time," replied he. "It's just starting. Watch that hypnotist."

They went through five horses, seven cows, eleven sheep, four pigs and a mixed lot of chickens, when a cow that had been absent when she was called was finally led up, very balky and frightened, a lovely little fat red and white cow, with, at her heels, the dearest little red and white calf, just able to stagger around.

"Here we are, ladies and gentlemen, cow with calf, the item No. 14 on the list, which was missing a moment ago," said the auctioneer, rolling his eyes and using the

126

high bull bellow. "This little cow was the life and soul of the late brother. A pet, a charming pet, a good milker, and this is her first calf which we see disporting itself about her."

I nudged Jim and went around to the front edge to have a look at the darlings.

"Jimmie," I said, "what a picture. An artist could paint this."

The auctioneer went into roars and bellows, and the little cow tugged and backed, and the calf came out in front and stared in glassy-eyed amazement at us. I looked up in the midst of the uproar and the auctioneer was staring at me darkly. He gave a little nod and I nodded back in a friendly way.

"Sold," roared the auctioneer, like a cannon going off, "sold to the little gentleman with the purple hat for thirty dollars, cow with calf. Next item, ladies and gentlemen."

I looked up dazedly at Jimmie.

"Keep your head still," hissed Jimmie. "At an auction sale hold your head like the knob on a banister post. Don't move a muscle."

"Jim, did I buy them?"

"You certainly did. I saw you."

"But, Jim, I only nodded back at him. He nodded to me as if he knew me."

"They're your cow and calf now."

I stood speechless. What the dickens would I do with a cow with calf?

Implements went next, and while I was standing there, still thinking of the cow with calf and not even hearing what was being sold, I happened to look up again. And again the auctioneer was staring fixedly at me, leaning slightly forward, his hand halfraised and his finger pointing at me. I half-smiled. He thrust his face forward and raised his busy eyebrows. I wasn't intimidated by him.

I winked at him.

"Sold," he roared, "sold set of harness to the little gentleman in the purple hat."

"Aw, I didn't, I didn't . . ."

"Shut up," hissed Jim. "You did. I saw you. You winked at him, of all the silly things."

"I was just kidding."

"A wink is as good as a nod," said Jimmie. "Anybody could tell you that, you sap. Now hold still. Don't even blink. Don't breathe if you catch him looking at you."

"Let's get out of here," I said.

"Just stand by a minute," protested Jim. "It's a sickle we came for."

Jimmie was amused at my troubles. I could feel him shaking periodically, as if he were laughing inside. He kept rubbing his hand over his mouth.

"It may be humorous to you," I said.

At the end of the implements came a lot of crops, including hay and ensilage and straw.

"Next we have," hoarsely roared the auctioneer, "one lot of hay, three tons, in the south pasture, stacked and of easy access for removal. This is pure alfalfa hay, finest quality . . ."

He roared on and got the price up to about a dollar a ton. Jim had another shaking fit. I was standing rooted to the ground, forcing myself not to look up, forcing myself not to make a sign or a sound.

"Sold," roared the auctioneer, "one stack of hay, about three tons to the tall gent with the pleasant smile."

I heard Jim gasp and I knew when I looked up at him that he had bought the hay.

"What did you do?" I asked.

"I just raised my hand to my face," said Jim, thinly.

"Jim, let's sneak away," I said. "Pretend we are just going to look at our purchases."

"Here comes the clerk," said Jim.

He took down Jim's name and address. He already had mine several times.

"We're just stepping over to look at the hay," said Jim.

Must Be Safer Way

We strolled to the back of the crowd. We went out to the lane beside the house. A thin, elderly man followed us.

"Excuse me, mister," he said, "that there set of harness you bought?"

"Yes, sir," said I.

"I been waiting twelve years for old Harry to pass away to get that harness, and I bid it way higher than it was worth."

"I might dispose of it if you had a sentimental interest in it," I assured him.

"Sentimental interest," cried the elderly farmer. "Heck, I tell you I been sitting right alongside of Harry here for forty years and when he bought that harness I said to myself I'll git that some day."

"Then it's yours for what I paid for it." I said. "Just tell the clerk to put your name in place of mine."

"Thankee," said the old farmer, agitatedly. "thankee. After waiting twelve years, you understand."

Our car, fortunately, was on the main road. Waiting for a particularly loud and hoarse uproar from the auctioneer, which meant a hot bid, we slipped down the row of cars in the lane, reached our car, started it and slipped cautiously away in low gear until we got out of sight.

"No sickle," I said.

"As a matter of fact," said Jim, "I didn't see a sickle in any of those job lots."

"Aren't there safer ways of buying a sickle?" I asked.

"Oh, sure, any hardware store," said Jim. "But I wanted you to see how thrilling it is to live on the farm."

"I guess it's the mystery of living on the farm that attaches people to the country," I said.

"That's it," said Jim. "It's like gambling. You don't know whether your crops will be droughted or whether it will be a bull calf or a heifer or whether the hens will get the seven-year itch. Farm life has all the fascination of gambling. It takes a terrible grip on you."

"You don't even know," I said, "when you are going to suddenly own a cow with calf."

"Or," said Jim, jealous of my set of harness, "a stack of hay."

So we reached the highway, and nobody was after us.

Each to His Trade

October 20, 1934

"Good-day, gentlemen," said the little financial man.

"My family," said Jimmie Frise, "are after me to clean the furnace pipes."

"It's a trifling job," I said. "My gardener does it in a few minutes each year and doesn't even mention it at the end of the month."

"Still," demurred Jimmie, "I don't see why I should rob some poor man of a dollar."

"It would do you good to engage occasionally in a little unpleasant toil," I said. "One of the things that is wrong with the world is specialization, not only in industry, but in life itself."

"How do you mean?" demanded Jim.

"We kick about the deadening effect of mass production," I stated, "and the evil effect upon the human race of having men doing one small thing over and over again all their lives, like screwing up nuts or tightening a bolt or some other automatic action. It drives men mad. But how about us all living our lives as automatically, never straying out of the rut, always doing the same things every day at the same time, getting out of bed the same side, shaving in the exact same way, starting with our top right cheek and ending with our left neck, kissing the same woman goodby each morning at the same place in the same hallway, and so forth."

"What has this got to do with stove pipes?" demanded Jim.

"The deadly routine of your life," I went on, "includes a furnace, and you stoke it and shake it, and remove the ashes and stoke it again. But the ghastly routine would be broken if, once in a while, you cleaned the pipes. It would be like getting out of bed the other side, and shaving your left neck first and ending with your right top cheek, and kissing somebody else goodby in the front hall. It would give you a fresh and sudden zest."

"I never heard anybody rave about furnace pipes the way you do," said Jimmie. "How about helping me with them?"

"I could ask my gardener to," I agreed.

"How about the ghastly monotony of your own life?" sneered Jim.

"I often shave backwards," I said. "And sometimes I kiss my little daughter goodby instead."

"If I clean the furnace pipes," said Jim, "it won't be for

131

any philosophic or psychopathic reason. It will be simply to save a buck. For five years now I have been trying to end the depression by spending all I made, by sharing my work with others, by hiring people on the slightest pretext to do my work for me. But I can't see it has made the slightest difference. So from now on I am going to be thrifty and careful like everybody else, and do all my own chores, and sole my own boots, and cut my own grass, and clean my own furnace pipes."

"And what will you do with the money you save?" I asked.

"I'll buy bonds," said Jim.

"That's patriotic," I assured him. "Instead of spending your dollars on small jobs like furnace pipes and your garden, you will lend it to the government to pay relief. Then, after they have paid relief to a few million people, you get your money back in ten years. Meantime, who paid the relief?"

"Don't confuse me," begged Jim. "I am trying to do the right thing by my country. My country wants cash. To lend it to them, I am going to cut down my spending. I am going to do my own furnace pipes."

"And the people you no longer help support," I argued, "will get your money just the same, only in relief."

"I suppose so," admitted Jim.

"Then," I demanded, "where does the money come from, twenty years from now, when the government pays you back the money they borrowed from you?"

"Look," said Jim, "I have five children. In twenty years they will all be grown up and making money. The government can reborrow from them to pay me back."

"I'd rather have my furnace pipes done by a pipe cleaner," I said. "It makes him happy. And it only costs me two dollars. It won't cost my grandchildren anything."

"But there will be five Frises to borrow from instead of only one," pointed out Jim. "It will be easier. That's what the government figures on. It will be easier to borrow by the time their note to me falls due."

"It looks to me," I said, "as if we were paying for having our pipes cleaned and cleaning them ourselves. It is all very confusing."

"I only want to do what is right," said Jim. "If they say spend, I spend. If they say save, I save."

"And if you spend, it's gone," I enlightened, "and if you save, it's loaned."

But Jimmie had risen from the steps of his house, where we had been sitting in the sunshine, and was staring at a little man walking down the street.

This little man was small and smudgy. Under his arm, he carried a roll of what appeared to be very dirty carpet, and from the ends of the carpet protruded filthy brushes on long wire handles.

"Speak of the devil," exclaimed Jimmie.

The little man passing, halted and in a deep English voice cried.

"'Ow's yer pipes?"

"Come up a minute," called Jimmie.

"A real chimney sweep, like in Dickens," I breathed to Jim.

The little man drew nigh and rested his roll of carpet.

"Are you a chimney sweep?" I asked excitedly, picturing him as one who has spent his entire childhood and infancy in the chimneys of Old London.

"No, sir," he said, with dignity, "I am a financial man, by profession, but during the present interregnum, as you might say, I am picking up what I can."

"You clean chimneys?" asked Jim.

"I clean furnace pipes," said the little man.

"How much do you charge?"

"Two dollars," said he.

"Two dollars!" cried Jim. "Two bucks just to rattle a few furnace pipes into an ash can! Man, you're crazy."

"It's quite a job," said the chimney man.

"Why, for two dollars I could drive my car from here to Montreal!"

"But your pipes would still be choked," said the small man, "when you got back 'ome."

"Two dollars! Why, that is ridiculous," said Jim. "Some of you people have no sense of proportion. Just because a job is a little unpleasant, you charge three

133

times what it is worth. My friend and I can do those pipes in a few minutes after supper."

"I shouldn't try it of an evening, sir," said the little man. "Professionally speaking."

"Thanks very much," said Jim, dismissing the small man, who hoisted his roll of carpet. "I had no idea."

And as the little man retired down the walk, Jim said: "Look here, you save Saturday afternoon, we'll do mine and yours both."

"Mine were done," I pointed out.

"Lend me a hand, just for the experience," said Jim. "I want to look into this business of small jobs. Two bucks!"

Saturday Jim drove me home from the office very kindly and then reminded me, as he let me out, to come over at 2 p.m.

It is curious how seldom one looks at a furnace. One visits it in the dark, shovels coal into a glowing hole, rattles a shaker, reaches up to a familiar doohickey and turns the draft on or off, and the furnace remains a dimly seen, faintly disliked, something to be admitted only part way into one's consciousness.

Jim and I surveyed his furnace in some awe. It was a bulging and somehow bow-legged sort of furnace. It was aged and scaley and corroded. There were bands or belts of clay around it that fell away like dust when you touched them. Everything was rusty and squeaked.

Dark Cloud of Endeavor

The pipes were fragile and sagged. When we slapped them, they felt soggy and stuffed.

"How long is it since you had your pipes cleaned?" I asked Jim, doubtfully.

"I don't recall them being cleaned."

"Why, you have been wasting fuel for years and haven't been getting a fraction of the British thermal units you should have been getting."

"You'd better take off your coat," said Jim, throwing his across the empty coal bin stall.

I stood ready while Jim stretched up and took firm hold of the joint of pipe that vanished into the cellar wall.

134

It was stuck. It was corroded.

He tapped it with a stick. He hammered it with the shaker handle. He punched a hole in it.

"Poof," said Jim, as a darkish mist filled the air.

"Get a couple of chairs, and we'll both take hold and twist," I suggested.

So Jim got on a box and I got on a chair, and we took firm hold of the pipe and twisted.

It was only a matter of a fraction of a second, but as the pipe came free, Jim, who was curved in one of those fantastic postures tall men can get into when doing the most commonplace things, lost his balance off the box and I felt a heavy and clumsy pipe slip from my grasp.

"Are you there, Jim?" I asked, from the depths of the inky darkness which had suddenly enveloped the furnace room.

"Curious—pfft—smell, isn't it—pfft!" said Jim from below.

"We had better go outside," I suggested.

"Take a section of pipe each," said Jimmie. "There are ash cans in the side drive."

I felt above and found a sagging section of pipe. It came fairly easily into my arms, but I felt a cool dry flood of something like talcum powder flow over my hands and wrists as I tilted the pipe level.

"Easy, there," said Jimmie, coughing.

By only half breathing, we got out of the cellar, dark as night, into the semi-gloom of the stairs, and preceding Jimmie, I carried the pipe to the side door. It was heavy. You can have no idea how neglected those pipes were. I saw a garbage can and I dumped the pipe smartly head first into the can.

A great whoof of midnight whirled into the bright afternoon air.

"Make way," gasped Jim, behind me, and as I turned, still marvelling at the fog, I beheld a devilish figure, black from head to foot, heave a section of pipe alongside mine into the ash can, and another and a vaster and a more deadly black cloud billowed into the air.

"Jimmie!" I cried. "You're filthy. What have you been doing?"

But I could tell by the red gape of Jim's mouth in his face that I, too, was soiled.

"You'll pay for cleaning this suit, young man," I assured him. The more you try to brush soot off, the worse you get. Especially if you are perspiring a little.

"Keep still," said Jim. "Wait till I think."

But from the rear of the house came screeches and screams and moans in a female voice. It was the next door neighbor. We ran around the corner, and there was a lady, her arms held over her head like the statue of victory, and she was staring transfixed at three large curtains or drapes of a silvery blue color, that were hanging on the clothesline, while the dark cloud of our endeavor slowly engulfed them like a fog.

"Dear, dear," said Jimmie, drawing me back from the corner.

Better Stay in the Rut

To the lady's screams were suddenly added loud, brief and profane shouts of a man.

It was the man whose house abuts the rear of Jim's place.

Head low to avoid the cloud, he came hurling over the fence and faced us.

"Look at that!" he roared. "Painted this morning, and now look at it!"

We could make out the back of his house. It was finished in white and light green. The cloud was aiming straight at it, and vanishing into the paint as cigarette smoke vanishes into an electric fan.

The lady was standing waiting.

"Ladies and gentlemen," said Jim, "I will make it right with you."

"They just came back from the cleaners," wept the lady, "and I was airing that smell off them before putting them up before dinner when my father-in-law is coming and we have roast chicken, and they cover the living room windows and now . . ."

"That job," interrupted the man, "cost me forty-eight dollars and to have the back done, by George, will cost you at least twenty. Twenty, I estimate. Yes, sir,

Each to His Trade

twenty would be a fair estimate."

There we stood, with the two pipe sections upended in the ash can, and with us the man and the lady, when we heard footsteps up the drive and the little man with the roll of carpet that we had seen last Wednesday joined us.

"Glory!" yelled Jim.

"Good day, gentlemen," said the little financial man.

"How did you turn up?" said Jim, trying to wring the little man's hand, but the little man evaded him.

"I overheard you say Saturday, so I just dropped around. I do quite a little business this way, whenever I hear of gents planning to clean their furnaces."

He laid his roll of brushes down in a business-like way.

"I'll give you $5 to clean all this up," cried Jimmie. "That is, if you can empty these two joints as well."

"It would have been better," said the little man, "if you had left the pipes. But I'll do what I can."

"Five dollars," said Jim.

"And a dollar and a half to clean this suit," I said.

"And a dollar and a half for this one," added Jim, looking down at himself.

"And twenty for the paint job," I calculated.

"And say three for the curtains?" contributed Jim.

The little man, who had trotted down the cellar, reappeared.

"You'll need new pipes," said he. "These are all rotted and pitted."

"How much?" asked Jim.

"I should estimate about two," said he.

"Total," said Jim, "thirty-three dollars."

He was very cheerful.

"Now you see," said Jim, "that it is best not to try to get out of the rut. Accept the ghastly monotony of your life. And don't try to be thrifty. It always costs you more in the end. Each man to his trade. I'm an artist. You're a writer. And this gentleman cleans furnaces."

"The furnace itself," said the little man, picking up his carpet roll, "isn't in bad shape."

137

Sabbatical

November 3, 1934

"As servants of the people," said Jimmie Frise, "we are not paying enough attention to the weightier problems of to-day."

"I guess we haven't got the equipment," I agreed.

"We waste our time," went on Jim, "making little unimportant experiments with pickling, furnace pipes, rabbit hunting and other minor domestic quarrels."

"I would love," I said, "to be a great authority."

"It is easy to become a great authority," stated Jimmie. "You just give up everything else, you forget about money, about your wife and family, you just concentrate yourself on one subject, like humming birds or radio tubes or something, and work sixteen hours a day at it and dream about it fitfully all night, year after year for thirty-five years. And then, when you are seventy-one

138

"If we were hoboes," said
Jimmie, "we could just climb
aboard a freight train and
dangle along through the
lovely country . . ."

years old and hump-backed and half blind and your family has all grown up and left you a quarter of a century ago, and you have no friends left, and you die, you get your picture in the papers and underneath it says, 'The great authority on humming birds.' "

"I don't mean that kind of authority," I hurried. "I mean a sort of authority that just comes by his knowledge instinctively, like poets—you know?—just born with an understanding of some of the mysteries of this life. I feel I have such an instinctive knowledge about the poor and oppressed. I sort of feel that, but for the grace of God and a little accident somewhere in my boyhood, I would have been a tramp myself."

"I often feel that way," mused Jim. "Sometimes I marvel that I have a house to live in."

"Maybe everybody feels that way," I suggested.

"I doubt it," said Jim. "I think you and I have a deep sympathy with bums because we know, deep in our hearts, that if it hadn't been for some guidance we got as children or some friendly expectation we felt from our elders, we would have been hoboes."

"If we were hoboes," went on Jim, "we could just climb aboard a freight train and dangle along through the lovely country and whenever we saw a beautiful lake or a lovely range of hills, all we have to do is jump off and stay there until our eyes and souls were filled. Maybe, by jove, maybe hoboes are artists at heart, poets and dreamers, who surrender all the world that they may saturate themselves in beauty!"

"And all the world to see," I cried. "There is no reason to suppose that a hobo does not appreciate landscape as much as we do, and we have to pay big money and reserve expensive berths and staterooms to go abroad to look at mountains and the sea."

It Ought to Be Law

"Most artists I know," I submitted, "look just one jump removed from hoboes."

"Did you ever hear of the Sabbatical year?" asked Jim.

140

"I probably did as a child," I guarded.

"In ancient Biblical days," says Jim, "every seventh year was a year of rest, like the seventh day. In the sabbatical year, nobody was allowed to work or till the earth. It was a year of rest. Some of the universities allow their professors a sabbatical year, and they go on holidays, with full pay, for the whole year!"

"I missed my calling," said I.

"The old Hebrews were a wise bunch," said Jimmie. "We make a big mistake when we aren't fundamentalists. We should take Moses whole. We should have never surrendered the sabbatical year. Every seventh year, every man in this world ought to be allowed to turn hobo. Bankers, mechanics, newspapermen."

"Where would you head for, Jimmie, if you turned hobo?"

"I'd head for California," said Jim. "First, I would go to California and visit Tia Juana and then, at the right season, I would amble across to Kentucky and see the Derby and lie around on the blue grass for a month or two. Then, maybe, I'd stow away for England and see Ascot. Ireland, I'd like to see Ireland too, and spend a couple of months around one of those famous studs where they raise Irish hunters. But what about you? What would you do?"

"I'd start my sabbatical year," I said, clearing my throat, "in May. I'd start via the Nipigon and then across to fish British Columbia, up to Alaska, finishing Alaska about August. Then I'd catch a boat for New Zealand, arriving there just as the brown and rainbow trout season opens about October first. I'd fish all around New Zealand until maybe February, and then stow away for the south of France, fishing through the Pyrenees and up and across into Devonshire by the first of April, then slowly, stream by stream, up to Scotland . . ."

"Wait a minute!" cried Jim. "Your sabbatical year is up!"

"Won't you let me catch one salmon in Scotland?" I asked indignantly.

"You've got to be back in Toronto on May first," stated

141

Jim. "But it is a swell idea, that sabbatical year."

"It ought to be law," I declared.

"We ought," said Jim, with that thoughtful, looking-away expression he wears when he is putting something over, "to just try a little of the hobo life, to see what it is really like. I mean, here we set ourselves up as the friends of the poor, but we don't bark our shins grabbing freights. How about some day putting on some old clothes and going for a short trip on a freight?"

And that is how it came about that last Monday Jimmie and I sneaked off at lunch hour and went home and put on our old hunting clothes and peak caps.

Grabbin' a Freight

"Better take a few dollars each to get home on," I suggested, as we admired ourselves in the mirror in Jim's hall.

"Not on your life," said Jim. "As artists, we must not only play the part of hoboes, we must be hoboes. Don't let us take more than about 30 cents each, in dimes."

"Suppose we get away off by Orillia or some place?" I inquired.

"Don't be silly," said Jim. "We aren't going more than twenty miles. Freights always stop at sidings. We'll go an hour or so one way, then hop off and catch another one coming into the city. Just to get a taste, not a belly-ful."

Jim had found out that one of the best places in the world to catch a freight is in the Mimico yards. There vast hundreds of acres of train tracks and sidings, thousands of empty box cars, long trains of loaded cars are assembled.

"We have to watch out for dicks," said Jim, as we headed for the railway yards.

"O-kay, boy," said I, slouching.

With caps pulled over our eyes and shoulders tough and legs kind of bowed, which is any man's way of feeling tough, we slunk through Mimico to Church St. and up to the subway. We were instantly in the core, the centre, the heart of railroadom. Turning in at the subway, we found ourselves in a vast region densely striped with hundreds of tracks and thousands of cars, with engines slowly puffing through, some drawing immense endless strings of cars, others steaming fussily about alone, and gauntletted railroad men, in overalls and peaked caps, leaning athletically out from cars and engines.

Hidden from us by strings of cars, engines puffed by us, and we heard the crunch of gravel under the feet of men which we could see by stooping down and looking under the cars. But they were railroad men's feet. No bums did we see in the half hour we spent prowling up and down.

Two tracks away, we heard a string of cars shunting.

"Dere's one haulin' cut, pardner," hissed Jim. "Let's scram on board, huh?"

We crawled underneath two strings of motionless freights and came out alongside the train that was still creaking from the shunt.

Three cars to our left, we saw an empty box car with its door ajar about two feet.

"Dere she is, buddy," hissed Jim. "Lemme see how smart you are at grabbin' a freight, huh?"

We scrunched low and made the dash.

Jim boosted me through the open door and swung himself inside with professional smoothness.

"She's headed west," said Jim. "That means either Detroit or maybe Winnipeg. We'll go as far as Brantford or Aurora."

Cr-rash! shunted the train. You could hear it coming, but still it nearly knocked you off your feet.

"These freights are rough," said I.

"You get used to it," said Jim, walking to the door to peek.

"Nix!" he hissed. "Flat against the wall! Here comes a brakeman!"

We hugged the wall of the freight car as we heard footsteps crunching nearer on the gravel.

The footsteps stopped. We held our breath.

Then the brakeman reached up and with a grunt slammed the car door shut, and we heard a metallic clink and he threw home some kind of a bolt or latch.

The footsteps died away.

"He locked us in!" I whinnied.

"Take it cool," said Jim. "We'll figure this out."

"But we may not get out until we get to Vancouver," I wailed, "or Des Moines!"

"We stop plenty of places," soothed Jim. "All we have got to do is holler."

"One brakeman and one engineer can't hear us holler half a mile away," I said loudly. "Let us holler now!"

"Hoy." roared Jimmie promptly. "HELP!"

"Help, HELP!" I echoed, kicking the wall of the box car.

I will not embarrass you with a full stenographic record of the noises, yells and signals that we engaged in for the next ten minutes. Then we stopped because we were hoarse.

"She hasn't started yet anyway," said Jim.

"Maybe, Jim," I said, as we sat on the floor, resting our lungs, "maybe this is one of those empty cars they store at Mimico until next summer."

"It might be," agreed Jim.

"Maybe nobody will come by," I quavered, "and we will die of hunger and thirst. And maybe this car will not be used until they move the wheat next July."

"Cut it out," warned Jim.

"And we will be missing until next August," I went on, "when they will find our desiccated and mummified bodies out in Weyburn, Sask.!"

The Free-Faring Life

"Stow it," warned Jim.

"We have no identifications in these clothes," I went on. "I'm going to spend what strength I have left now in carving my name on the wall of this box car, Jimmie, and if I am spared long enough, by the pangs of hunger and thirst, I will carve on the wall the details of our horrible experience. So people will know what became of us."

An engine came puffing in the distance.

"Get ready," cried Jim, leaping up in the dark. "Hoy, HOY, HAAALLLPPP!"

But the engine went thundering and hissing by.

"No use," said I, sadly. "Let us save our strength and listen for footsteps. Surely some bum will come by."

So we sat and listened. Occasionally, to break the monotony of conversation, we hallooed and yelled.

"It must be getting evening," surmised Jimmie.

At about what must have been nine o'clock by the silence of the world, broken only by the thunder of passing trains, Jim suggested we take turns at having a little sleep. I slept first. But cinders are poor mattresses. I woke to find Jim snoring by my side.

"HAAALLLP!" I roared, but really to wake Jim.

"It must be getting towards morning."

Engines went by, trains, long, long trains went by, going to Winnipeg, Vancouver and Des Moines.

"This," said Jim, heavily, "might be one of those silk trains that make non-stop runs across the continent."

"It is like being lost in the middle of the Sahara desert," I said, hollowly. "Here, in the midst of a great freight yard, on the edge of a mighty city, we are lost as if we had flown in a rocket to the moon!"

We dozed again.

"Clink!"

We both sat up to face a foot-wide strip of God's morning light streaming in and dazzling us. We made out the head of a man, a villainous, stubble-covered face peering at us with amazement.

"Hullo", said he. "Did I startle ye?"

Jim and I swallowed, poising for a spring.

"Kin I come in?" he asked, reaching up for a hoist.

"We're getting out," said Jim.

"All right," said the hobo, "make it snappy. She's just about to pull."

Jim and I went through the narrow crack together. The tramp hoisted himself up and in.

"I hope yer not leavin' on my account," said he, looking down at us.

"No, no," we assured him.

We hurried toward the Church St. subway.

"Ah," cried Jim, as we hastened down toward the street cars in the fresh dawn, "the free-faring life of the hobo!"

But I was thinking about bacon and eggs and I didn't want to be interrupted.

Flying
Trapeze

December 29, 1934

"Aaaaaaghhh," said Jimmie Frise.

"What is it?" I asked anxiously.

"Ughh," groaned Jimmie, "this Christmas-New Year's week gets me down. Over eating. Over eating. I feel like a boa constrictor that has eaten three goats. One goat. Two goats. Three goats."

"Yes," I said, "I know that lumpy feeling."

"I could just lie down somewhere and let those colossal gorgings digest," said Jimmie. "I feel drowsy. Or is it just that I have eaten so much, my skin is tight all over me, and that is what is making my eyes half close?"

"What we need," I declared, "is exercise."

"I never felt less like exercise in all my life," replied Jim, resting himself in another slouched position on his chair.

With thoughts of the gymnasium turning over in our mind, we polished off the remains of the turkey . . .

"Big meals," I said, clearing my throat, "big meals, Jimmie, should be forbidden by the public health legislation of this country. They should be a crime. In ancient times, when nature was our only law, men, like any other animal, ate whenever they could, but lots of times they went for days and days without a bite to eat."

"I wish I was starving to death right now," moaned Jimmie.

"Lots of times," I went on, "when game was scarce, whole tribes of men were slowly starving to death. Then all of a sudden, a herd of prehistoric reindeer or a couple of mammoths came along . . ."

"Ughh," protested Jimmie.

"A herd of mammoths came along," I continued, "and the whole tribe rushed out of the caves and slew a couple of them. And what a feast there was then! Up leaped the fires, and great juicy steaks of mammoth went on the pointed sticks to be roasted . . ."

"Please, please," begged Jimmie, rising. "If you don't change the subject, I'll have to leave."

"Very well," I said. "But you see the point. Mankind, in the long-drawn-out early history of us, used to feast only after long fasts. I should say that in the ancient days mankind ate, as a rule, very little, and only once in a long while did they get a square meal. In these days, when we all eat regular meals, we should never, never feast."

"Agreed, agreed," said Jim, yawning and groaning at the same time.

"Having all and more than we need to eat, as often as we like," I said, "it is against the ancient law of nature for us to gorge ourselves. It should be a public crime to stuff."

"I'm a criminal all right," said Jim, closing his eyes heavily.

"I'm a criminal, too," I assured him. "Christmas Day, I started with two fried eggs and bacon, toast, cherry jam, two mugs of coffee and a beaker of orange juice. Then, about two p.m., we sat down to a turkey. Such a turkey. I ate three full-size slices off the breast, cut with a sharp knife. A gobbin of dressing about the size of a grapefruit . . ."

"Erp," said Jim, "pardon me."

"Then mashed potatoes with dark bright brown gravy, and turnips and cranberry sauce with the skins left in, for sharpness . . ."

Planning a Cellar Gym

"You were saying," said Jim, heaving himself to an upright posture in his chair, "something about exercise. Talk about exercise. Tell me about walking five miles in the crisp winter afternoon, amidst bright pine trees along the frosty roads."

"Walking," I said, "about 120 to the minute, short, strong-legged paces, swinging a cane, with a tartan muffler around your neck, a pipe in your mouth, and steam blowing from your nose."

"Aaaahhhh," sighed Jimmie, looking better already.

"And big stout boots on your feet," I pictured, "and the ground frozen and lumpy underfoot, and chickadees and maybe a redpoll or two in the trees for you to pause and look at, and maybe a pheasant, all dark and burnished, running across the road ahead of you."

"Get away from pheasants, raw or roasted," warned Jim.

"In the olden days," I stated, "when we used to alternate feasts with long periods of enforced fasting, we got plenty of exercise. Hunting the mammoths must have been an arduous sport. Through bogs and swamps and through terrible jungles, with your poor stomach flat against your backbone from emptiness."

"Beautiful," murmured Jim.

"And you weary from carrying an immense club studded with bronze nails to kill the mammoths with."

"Keep the mammoths alive," urged Jim. "A dead mammoth gags me somehow."

"I tell you what," I suggested, "let's go for a good walk right now. Let's lock the office and go. Let's drive as far as the Jail Farm and then go for a big tramp about five miles west along one of those lovely winter York county dirt roads."

"I'd die," said Jim. "I'd just sit down by a snake fence and die. I haven't enough strength in my legs right now

149

to stand up."

"The only thing to cure you," I informed him, "is exercise. A brisk, long walk. A swinging walk through country with cold wind in your face and pushing against your chest."

"It's lovely to hear about," said Jim, "but I couldn't do it. Just let us talk about exercise."

"Can't we do something about exercise?" I asked. "Instead of merely talking about?"

"I've often thought," pursued Jim, "of making a sort of private gymnasium in my cellar. It's a big cellar, with a nice high ceiling. I could erect a horizontal bar, and rings on ropes, you know?"

"And my wife," I said, "has one of those rowing machines stored in the attic. I'd lend it."

"And a horse," said Jim. "You know those leather horses for leaping over."

"Why don't we just join a gym?" I asked.

"It's too public," demurred Jim. "I couldn't bear showing off my shape in front of a lot of beautiful young fellows built like gods."

"You're right," I said. "Make it a cellar gym."

"There," said Jim, relaxing a little, "we two could meet of an early morning, fresh from sleep and before starting for the office. We could do a crisp half hour of swinging and whirling. We could shake all the stale blood out of our limbs."

"And heads," said I.

"We could start our pulses working," went on Jim. "Evenings, we could do tricks, slowly reviving the lost talents of our muscles. Saturdays we could hold private and personal gymkhanas, competing with each other to see who had the most strength, the most skill."

"You have me interested," I admitted.

So that when we broke off work early and went home in the bright afternoon, we called at my house and got the rowing machine out of the attic of my house, and I also contributed a length of big half inch rope that once I bought for an anchor, not knowing how big half-inch rope really is. An old army saddle I also dug out of the attic, relic of my war days when I tried to ride horses.

"This," I explained to Jimmie, "will do instead of a
gymnasium horse. We can prop it up some way between
two chairs or something."

Jim had timber to make horizontal bars. Old curtain
poles of the kind all houses used to have between the living room and the dining room, and all of which are now
stored in the attics of the world, Jim produced and we
made series of bars on which we could swing like Tarzan,
from limb to limb, strengthening our arms and dilating
our chests and lungs.

Jimmie's stuffiness passed off as we got the material
assembled in his cellar.

"I feel better already," said Jim, removing his coat and
vest and producing an old box full of hammers, saws,
nails and dusty old brackets and things.

First we had to sit down to plan it. We sat down on
boxes and planned, with gestures. Over in the corner
would be the rowing machine. Along the back of the big
cellar would be a series of parallel bars for swinging,
grand circles, short arm balances and chinning.

"I haven't," said Jim, "chinned myself for so long, it
will be a treat to do it again."

"And rings," I cried. "Jimmie, when I was at school, I
could travel faster around the rings than any boy in the
school. I love rings. To swing at arm's length on rings,
gaining momentum and speed. I wonder if we couldn't
get so expert, we could set up two sets of ropes and
rings, and swing from one to the other, like trapeze artists?"

"Vaulting the horse," said Jim. "Now there's a thing
that tests your mettle. You take a run at the horse, place
one hand on the saddle, and vault cleanly over it. I would
rather see a man vault the horse than see a whole team
of military jumpers take the hurdles on horseback."

So we planned. We would have the horse in the middle
of the cellar. I got up and set boxes and things and rested
a broom across, and balanced my old saddle on the broom
to show Jimmie just how it would look. Then I sat down
again.

"It isn't big enough," mused Jim, "for a running track
down here. But we might get some whitewash like they

use on tennis courts and mark off the floor in rings and squares, to make it look gymnasiumy. You know, half the inspiration of a gymnasium is the look of it. It must look appetizing."

"I thought you were tired of appetite," I said.

"Now, how about a chest expander," said Jim, shifting on to the floor and resting his back against the box. "We could attach a couple of bricks to some strong sash cord, and run it up through pulleys. A first-rate chest expander."

"Swell," said I. "And how about a rubbing-down table? I could rub you down and then you could rub me down."

For Fresh Inspiration

"Boy," said Jimmie, "that rub-down makes me feel good. What would we use for a rub-down?"

"Liniment," I decreed. "A good cool stinging liniment. With a pungent, turpentiney odor."

"Ach," said Jim, "the smell of it fairly catches my breath. I feel like a new man already, just thinking about it."

He sat up and stretched. He stood up. He walked around the cellar and patted the saddle.

"Think," he said, "of that grand fresh feeling of doing twenty minutes fast work on these bars, those rings, that horse, then five minutes on the rowing machine, then a quick rub-down with liniment and so to work!"

"I tingle," I assured him. "Try a few pulls on that rowing machine."

Jim stood above the rowing machine, looking down at it.

"Sit on it," I urged him. "Take a few pulls and see how strong and elastic those springs are."

"In a few minutes," said Jim. "I've got to run upstairs for a second."

Left alone, I lay there visualizing the gymnasium. Seeing Jimmie and me in our underwear lithely whirling and twisting, swinging and bending and wheeling. Upstairs I heard Jim's feet to and fro in the kitchen.

He came down, just as the light from the cellar windows was fading, with a large tray.

On the tray were onion sandwiches and the tail end of the turkey. The onion sandwiches were Spanish onions sliced thin, as only Jimmie knows how to make them, with salt and pepper, a dash of vinegar laid on with a teaspoon to get it just right, a faint dash of wooster sauce, between well-buttered thin bread.

The turkey was on its last legs, but hidden about its colossal carcase were large gobbets of meat, some white, some dark. Inside were large hunks of dressing still adhering to the ribs.

Jim had also a pot of coffee and a jug of thick cream.

"Ah," said I, sitting forward.

We just laid the tray on the gymnasium floor and sat to it on our boxes.

After we had finished, I locked my fingers behind my head and leaned back against the wall.

"Well," I said, "how about the gymnasium? How about doing something for a start?"

"New Year's dinner will be in a few days," said Jim, picking a last thread of white meat off from along that big keel bone sticking up drily. "What do you say if we wait until after New Year's before going on with the gym? It will be a sort of fresh inspiration for us?"

"O-kay," I agreed.

So before going upstairs to listen to the radio from the chesterfield and the big fat chair to match it, we pushed the bars and ropes and boards and saddle and stuff into a corner where they would be handy.

Unworthies

January 5, 1935

"Psst," said Jimmie Frise. "Look at this guy."

We were walking along King street back to the office.

A scarecrow, cringing from the wintry wind, was hugging the tall buildings, and from under his capbrim he was anxiously scanning the passers-by.

We drew near. The scarecrow sighted us. Pulled himself together. He fell in beside us.

"Excuse me, Mac," he mumbled. His face was bloated and boiled looking. His eyes were sunken. "Spare a guy a bite to eat. I ain't et—"

"How much?" said Jim, cheerily. "Two bits?"

The scarecrow snatched the coin from Jimmie. With scarcely a gesture, much less a word of thanks, he cringed into the biting wind and sped away. We looked after him. He was a ragged, shambling caricature even of a bum. But he sped away as if filled with a mighty purpose.

"Jimmie," I said, "you're a sap. That, if ever I saw one, was an undeserving case. An unworthy case. He looked as if he had just risen up out of a ditch where he had lain drunk all night. A horrible specimen."

"He was unworthy," said Jim, gently. "That's why I gave him two bits."

"Because he was unworthy?" I gagged.

"Exactly," repeated Jimmie. "Because he was unworthy. In this town are a thousand agencies of state and church, municipal and national, amateur and professional, for the care of the worthy and the deserving. But there is no place for the unworthy and the undeserving. There is no place for that man."

And we looked back again, into the biting wind. But he was gone.

"Jimmie," I said, "I hadn't thought of that."

"That's what we have to think about now," stated Jim. "We have everything solved. We know the cause of all our troubles. We are planning the remedies. We have planned recovery. We have official government relief. It

As we walked through the wind and sleet, we met a panhandler. Our hearts leaped. "Could you spare—" he began . . .

is part of the scheme of things now. But outside all of it there are the unworthy, the undeserving. Now somebody has to come along and look after the unworthy."

"It sounds funny," I assured Jim. "It's a new idea."

"It's an old idea," argued Jim. "There once was a great Teacher who said He did not come to save the worthy, but the unworthy, and who went first amongst the publicans and sinners, who sought out the bums and the street walkers. I don't think He even once mentioned planned economy or relief. He just went around and touched with His hand dead men and gave them life, diseased men and healed them, lepers, the scum of the earth."

"I see," I admitted.

"Suppose," said Jimmie, "we start a society for the assistance of the unworthy and undeserving?"

"Wonderful," I cried.

"Suppose we just organize a little society of a couple of dozen of us that feel the same way we do about things,"

155

went on Jimmie, "a society that takes just as much trouble to make sure the applicant is unworthy as the social workers take to make sure their cases are deserving?"

Starting a New Society

"We could maybe hire a social worker, a girl," I added, "who could have a little office. It wouldn't cost much."

"No," said Jim. "Our secretary would have to be some worthless failure of a guy, a complete and unreclaimable wreck of a man, whose investigations of each case would have to be doubtful and themselves not very reliable. What I want isn't a half-way sort of society. I would like to see our society itself unworthy. It's very unworthiness would have to appeal to those of us who were the supporting members."

"We could go out and ask the social welfare people who is the most undeserving man in Toronto and hire him." I suggested.

"Perfect," said Jim. "Perfect. Our office would be the shabbiest and dirtiest little office we could find in downtown Toronto. The secretary would have to be a loathsome object, with a jail record preferred. To him would come all the most unworthy cases in the city, the ones without a single thing to be said to their credit. They would be the perpetual drunks, the wife deserters, the petty thieves. No big thief could get a cent of aid. Just the miserable thieves, the cowardly, creeping thieves."

"I begin to see the beauty of it," I breathed.

"It is beautiful," said Jim. "But it is more than that. It is the secret at the bottom of all our human troubles today. We base our entire human society on worthiness. It's wrong."

"We have to adopt some standard," I submitted.

"We don't," said Jim. "That's where we make the first mistake. That's the wrong alley we turn up into, right at the start. Jesus didn't ask Lazarus what he believed in. He just raised him, knowing that when he was risen he would believe."

"I wasn't taught that way," I protested.

"Can't you read?" retorted Jimmie.

We went up to Jimmie's studio in the tiptop of The Star and looked across the world fogged with driving snow and a wind that blew grimly from the Pacific to the Atlantic.

"Out there," said Jim, "the ones to worry about are the undeserving. An unworthy man, it seems to me, gets colder than a worthy man. And hungrier. It helps keep a man warm if he knows he is worthy."

"I suggest," I said, "we pick out about thirty or forty of our friends and start a little group for the assistance of the worthless."

"You draft a letter," said Jim. "We can send it around to a select bunch. Let's call a meeting for some day next week. If enough turn out we can organize a group and draw up a set of resolutions."

So while Jimmie worked at his cartoon I drafted a beautiful and impassioned letter. I wrote and rewrote and tugged at the heartstrings and brought tears even to my own eyes. I read bits to Jimmie. He nodded and went on scratching.

When the letter was done I read it all, standing up and using gestures. Jim and I were both deeply moved. We both blew our noses and frankly wiped our eyes.

Hunting Undeserving Cases

"That's a beautiful letter," said Jimmie. "It's a classic."

"Now we can have it mimeographed," I said.

"Wait a minute," interrupted Jimmie. "Just a minute. We don't want to go off the deep end. We want to have some idea of the number of the undeserving cases. How many really undeserving cases are there in town? One hundred? Five hundred?"

"Perhaps the social service people could tell us?" I offered.

"They sort out the worthy," stated Jim. "Let us find the unworthy ourselves."

"How?"

"I can find ten between here and the Market," said Jim.

So we went along King street in the wind and sleet.

157

We saw numbers of poorly-dressed men and one old woman. But she had a bunch of pencils in her hand, offering them timidly from a damp and ill-sheltered niche in one of the big buildings.

"No, no," whispered Jim, when I paused. "She's trying to make a few cents. She's a worthy case."

We went on. Up until Yonge street, we had found none at all.

"It takes a worthy man to be out at all on a day like this," I said. "All the unworthy are sheltering somewhere, sneaking into missions and things."

At Toronto Street we met a panhandler. Our hearts leaped.

"Could you spare—" he began.

"Are you a worthy case?" we demanded. "Do you drink? Do you support a wife and children . . . ?"

The poor chap broke down and moved aside into the shelter of a building.

"I have a wife and child," he said. "I spend the mornings collecting scraps of wood and junk to keep the fire going while I—"

"Sorry," we said, leaving him.

Between Toronto Street and the Market we met three more. One of them was quite tipsy, but he said he was going back to a good job with his older brother as soon as he sobered up. The other two were both willing to work and showed by their calloused hands that they had jobs lately.

"Would you work in a ditch?" we demanded.

"Lead us to it," they cried, heartily.

So we left them.

"We'll have to go to some mission or some place," I said. "That's where the unworthy will be cringing on a day like this."

"It will be like poaching," said Jim, "but we will go."

We dropped in on a mission not far from the Market. There were fifteen men in it at the time. Some were scrubbing floors, some were making stew, others were making beds, one old man was darning socks for his comrades. A young man was lying very ill on a cot and three men were down in the big room around the piano, singing softly.

"What are you singing for?" I asked. "Is this a worthy pastime when all your comrades are working?"

"We're rehearsing for a concert to-night," said the man at the piano. "We expect a full house the way the weather is."

A Box Car Club

Jim was already tugging my sleeve, so we went on the streets again. Along Queen we walked. Two very young chaps, extremely chilled looking and ragged, responded to our friendly eye by pausing.

"Well, boys," said Jim. "You look kind of peaked."

"How about something to eat?" asked the larger boy.

"Where are you from? Toronto?" I asked.

"No, sir, we're trying to get to Owen Sound," said the big one. "We've come this far from Montreal."

"How?"

"Riding freights."

"In this weather?"

"Well, it got too bad yesterday, so we laid off until it gets milder."

"Do you live in Owen Sound?"

"I don't, but the kid does," said the bigger one. "We met in Montreal trying to get a job on a ship. That was last September we met. We didn't get a ship. So finally the kid said he wanted to get home to see his mother for Christmas, and I said I'd get him home. But we kind of got away to a bad start. We got pinched at Prescott and laid up ten days. However, I'll get him home before all the goose is eaten."

The younger boy turned a pale color.

"No, Jimmie," I said. "These boys are both worthy. They were both trying to run away to sea. Then the one tried to get home for Christmas. And the other one was trying to help him."

"Very deserving," said Jim. "I would like to do something for you, boys, but it is against our principles."

The older boy smiled thinly and the young one turned away.

159

In silence we walked toward Yonge street and just as
we turned into Yonge who should we see creeping close
along the tall walls of the buildings but the same worthless bum that Jimmie had treated to a quarter at noon!
We stood in front of him.

"Ha," said Jim. "Here we are again!"

"How about something to eat?" asked the bleary-eyed
bum. "I ain't et—"

"I gave you a quarter at noon," said Jim. "What did
you do? Drink it?"

The dreadful looking man rubbed his nose with the
back of his hand.

"Listen," he begged, "your're the only touch I've made
all day. There I got seven guys in a box car. One bottle of
cat costs forty cents."

"What's cat?" I asked.

"Catawba," said the bum, "wine. There I got seven
guys in a box car. We gotto have our rum issue when we
go to sleep, don't we? We're old soldiers, see? We're
used to havin' a shot of rum in lieu of a hot meal, see? In
loo of. So it's my job to rassle one bottle of cat a day,
that's for bedtime, and another guy he gets bread and
whatever else is going, see, and another guy he's got to
get hay for the floor, and another guy tobacco. We each
got our department, see?"

"What is this, a society?" Jimmie asked.

"A kind of society, captain," said the bum, shuddering
down into his collar. "A sort of society of bums, the ones
that ain't worthy, see, the undeserving, see? We just
give up, we can't get anywhere, so we just clubbed up.
My job is to get a bottle of cat, see, and it costs forty
cents, and all I got is your two bits. It'll be dark soon, so
I got to work up here."

"Just a second," said Jimmie, "I think you're a liar."

The bleary eyes opened and showed two icy gray
pupils that stared steadily into Jim's eyes.

"I'm a lotta things, captain, but I ain't no liar," said the
bum.

"You look as if you had been on a drunk for a week,"
stated Jim, staring back.

"Oho, that!" laughed the bum, revealing crooked

160

teeth. "Oho, me face? My eyes? Oho, that's hay fever!"

"Hay fever? In mid-winter?" scoffed Jim.

"Sure, you sleep in hay and see what you get, even in winter," said the bum, hotly.

"That's right, Jim," I hastened. "Every time I change the hay in the dog kennel, even in winter, I get an attack."

"Oho, so that's what you was thinking?" laughed the bum. "The boys was saying last week that somebody else ought to have the rum issue to look after. They said I looked like a jag even when I was praying for Daffy Baird."

"Praying?"

"One of the guys is Daffy Baird," said the bum. "He got shell shocked in the war and every once in a while he starts crying. He's a little off, you understand; he's not all there, see? So the only thing stops him is me praying. I stand up over him and pray. I used to be good at imitating a preacher, see? So I pray and pray and pretty soon Daffy shuts up and we can all go to sleep."

"That would be quite a sight," said Jim.

"Where's your box car?" I asked.

The bum looked sharply at me.

"Well, gents, thanks for the two bits," he said.

"Look here," cried Jim. "I'd like to fix you boys up with a real feed. Suppose you let us come down and see your place, and we can bring a load of stuff with us we can get in the store here; we'll make it a surprise party."

The bum was shoving past us. His face had set again into a bleary mask.

"Nuttin doing," he muttered.

"Half a minute," I said after him.

But he started fast and although we walked back to the corner of Queen he was swallowed up in the five o'clock throngs.

"I guess he thought we might be informers or busybodies," I suggested.

"He figured we weren't worthy," corrected Jim.

And we got back to The Star without finding anybody unworthy but ourselves.

Gun Shy

January 19, 1935

Screams filled the air as the old bag gave way and a mountain slide of pistols, of revolvers, fat and bulgeous, slewed and sprawled over the pavement of Bay Street

162

"We had better," said Jimmie Frise, "register our pistols."

"Nonsense," I replied. "I'm an officer of his majesty's Canadian militia. I'm an officer of the reserve. I am entitled to possess my arms."

"The new law," stated Jimmie, "says that every pistol or revolver—every—shall be registered with the police."

"That means bohunks and shady characters," I insisted. "It doesn't mean officers and gentlemen. Say, listen, I've carried that pistol of mine through some of the greatest battles in human history: Vimy, Passchendaele, Amiens. It is my armor, just the same as the armor of the Crusaders. Just the same as the swords of the knights of King Richard the Lion Heart. Do you think I'll submit to having my armor listed by a bunch of cops? No, sir."

"You are liable to a fine of fifty dollars if you don't," said Jim.

"I think this is an outrage," I declared hotly. "When there was a war they went through the streets with bugles and drums, begging me to come to the rescue of my native land. They thrust a pistol in my hands. Pleaded with me to use it often and truly. I marched through the world in those days with a pistol on my belt. Now they treat me like a suspect and demand that I register the same gun. I won't do it."

163

"It's just a matter of form," explained Jim.

"There is too much matter of form these days," I roared. "The world has got the jitters. Do they think I am a Red?"

"They never can tell," said Jim. "How do they know but that you may have changed your mind about things this last fifteen years since the war? In case of trouble which side of the barricades do they know you will be on?"

"The fact that my pistol is registered won't make any difference which side of the barricades I'll be on," I contended.

"No, but it will make a big difference to the cops that have got to rush around the city snatching up all the registered pistols, just in case," argued Jim. "I don't blame the cops. They'll feel a lot easier if they know just where the guns are."

"Caesar said," I announced, "that it was easy to raise an army, but it was terribly hard to disband one. This is the disbanding. This last shameful act. This causing the old and broken knights to come to the police station and register their arms. I'm through. I give in. They don't trust me any more. I'm just another suspect. They want to register my gun. All right. I'm through. They can fight their own wars from now on. They can employ registered soldiers and registered guns. I wouldn't fight for a nation whose idea of statesmanship is registration of everything. I wouldn't fight for a nation that would submit to such an indignity."

"Then you'll give up your guns?" asked Jim.

"I won't," I shouted. "I'll take them, and all my sons will come with me, and I'll throw them into the Humber. I'll make a ceremony of it. My little sons will stand by me, and one by one I'll throw my guns and my spurs and my Sam Browne belt and all the other things I've got left of those great and mighty days into the deepest hole in the river rather than submit them to the shame, the ignominy of being registered by a suspicious-eyed cop."

New Ideas Come This Way

"I've often heard you speak far differently about pistols," said Jimmie. "I've heard you say you never used your pistol. That pistols are of no use except for suicide or murder."

"Quite true," I admitted, "with this one exception: that in the middle of a battle, when you are scared stiff, a great big pistol in your hand gives you a lot of encouragement. If you bang it off in the air every few minutes, it encourages you."

"Did you never use it on the enemy?" asked Jim.

"I've no doubt the noise of my pistol—it was a big forty-five, firing a slug of lead the size of the end joint of your thumb and making a noise like a double-barrelled shotgun—I've no doubt the noise of my forty-five, added to the general racket of the war, helped to demoralize the Germans," I said. "But I doubt if I could hit a barn with my pistol even if I was in the barn with the door shut."

"Then," demanded Jimmie, "what is your objection to having the blame thing registered?"

"It is a moral question," I explained. "I think nothing of pistols. They are vicious and useless things. Fit for nothing but crime. But I have a pistol. It is mine. It is the mineness of the pistol, not the pistolness, that I am defending."

"You're a die-hard Tory," decreed Jim. "Don't you recognize, in this new law registering all pistols, the dawn of Communism in our government? Can you not see the wonder of Toronto's police, who less than four years ago were slugging Communists in parks, now so converted to Communism that they are adopting one of the main planks of the Communists?"

"Well," I said.

"Certainly," went on Jimmie. "The only difference is that the Communists started by confiscating factories and banks. We have started by confiscating pistols. It's all the same. It's the start. The fact that they register your property gives you a license to possess it. The next thing they do is revoke the license. Your property is thereby confiscated. It is very simple."

"Well I'll be!" I said.

"Yes," agreed Jim. "In Russia, they started at the big

165

end and are working down. In Canada we are starting at the little end, and are working up. It is all out of deference to some of our older gentlemen. In Russia, they haven't the same respect for elderly gentlemen we have in Canada. So, out of respect for these old gentlemen, they are starting confiscation with your pistol. After the old gentlemen pass away, they will then confiscate their factories and trust companies. See?"

"Who would think our police are like that, from looking at them?" I gasped.

"It's very simple," said Jim. "New ideas always come that way. We resist them at first. Then all of a sudden, we just slump."

"Well, I think as much of my pistol as a lot of old gentlemen think of their factories," I declared. "By which I mean, it's mine."

"That's it," said Jim. "How many pistols have you?"

"Well," I said, "I have my big army forty-five and a Luger automatic I got off a German. Then I have an old frontier Colt dating back to about 1870, but still capable of bumping off a buffalo at the gallop. I also have a little twenty-two trapper model I carry on fishing trips. And an old thirty-two pocket gun somebody gave me because they were afraid their children might get hold of it."

Carrying Down the Hardware

"How on earth are you going to carry all those openly down to the police station to get them registered?" cried Jim.

"I'll just send in a list," I said.

"The police want to see them," said Jim. "It is against the law to carry concealed weapons. So you'll have to carry them openly. I can see you walking along with two fistfuls of gats of all sizes."

"Ridiculous," I said. "The streets of Toronto crowded with people carrying revolvers!"

"It would have been a queer sight four years ago," said Jim. "But it's all right now. I've just got the one gat. When will we take them down?"

"Under protest, I'll go any time," I said.

Jim had an old suitcase which his family said he could

borrow for the purpose of transporting a load of greasy guns. We loaded it up with the hardware.

"Where do we take them?" asked Jim, hoisting the bag. It bulged. My old forty-five weighs nearly four pounds.

"I suppose to the city hall," I said. "It's handier. We can deliver them on the way to work."

We put the suitcase in the car and drove down town. Even at nine o'clock in the morning it is hard to find a parking place near the city hall. We drove around the block twice and at last got a spot on Richmond St. over near the vendor's which doesn't open until ten.

"Here," I said, "they're mostly mine. Let me carry it."

Along to Bay we lugged the bag. Jim was nervous.

"In a town like Toronto," he said, "it is a creepy business carrying a suitcase full of guns."

As we came to the corner, a large armored bank truck, defying all traffic laws, swung slowly around the turn, and behind it came two motor cars full of policemen, then a mounted cop and one motorcycle man. As if by magic, foot constables appeared on all four corners and stood like statues, while the august chariot of commerce and industry, in defiance of red lights, and calmly forcing common citizens in their cars to skid and slither out of the way as best they could, made the grand turn.

"Jimmie," I said, "the bag's a little heavy. Would you take it for a minute?"

"I have a sore hand," said Jim. "Wait until I get my glove on."

The whole city was filled with police. From the opposite direction, as we stood waiting for the lights to turn and for the traffic jam resulting from the bank car to solve itself, another stately steel fortress on wheels came to the corner, also accompanied by carloads of cops, with horse, cycle and foot police in attendance. And through the confusion of this mighty but daily spectacle in Toronto's downtown, Jimmie and I, with the bag of pistols, threaded our timid way.

Our hearts were in our mouths.

"Easy," whispered Jim anxiously.

I could hear the pistols rattling loudly in the bag. I looked at the bag. It was old. The handle seemed about to part. The walls of the bag bulged and I could see the shape of guns, of muzzles and cylinders, of trigger guards and butts, revealing themselves plainly.

"O-o-o-oh," I murmured.

A Cataclysmic Moment

Jim clung closely and protectingly over me. Police were everywhere, in cars, tooting at us, on horseback, clattering with fierce hoofs on the icy pavement of Bay and Richmond, on motorcycles, and, in massive great-coats and towering fur caps, looming on every side.

And curious crowds, caught in the daily pomp and circumstance of the parade of the armored bank trucks, gathered at all the corners of the street. Strange how people make way for Money. Strange how those homely steel lorries with faces peering from the bullet-proof windows, create a sense of awe in a more or less civilized city like Toronto. In the Middle Ages, a duke or a cardinal went by in his guarded carriage, and we, the people, stood agape on the corners. Nowadays, a duke or a cardinal would have to take his chances along with the rest of us. But the Money wagons, with a large constabulary hand raised on high in a grave reproof to all us rabble on the corners, is color blind, goes against the traffic lights, makes left hand turns where left hand turns are illegal, and we, with lumps in our throats and reverence in our eyes, make obeisance to the homely, the bullet-proof, the barred and blind-faced gods of to-day.

For us, it was a debilitating moment. As the bank trucks wheeled south, Jim and I started across the intersection, feeling as if all eyes were on us instead of on the solemn procession of the much-guarded money. If anyone knew, at this moment, in such a place, what we had hidden in this old brown bag!

A motor car backfired.

"Yarp!" I emitted.

"Look out!" hissed Jim, as I caught my balance.

But it was slippery. The bag had been for long years in the Frise family. The handle had been on too many trips

to the railroad station in the back of democrats and sur-
reys and phaetons with fringe around the tops. Rain had
rained on the old bag, and snow had silted on it as it
stood on Birdseye Center station platform at Christmas.
And summer sun had eaten mercilessly into its fibre as it
rode in launches on Lake Scugog or ridden in rumble
seats all over central North America.

I felt it give.

I set it down as hastily as I could to save the crash.

The bump was too much for the old frayed straps and
buckles.

"Jimmie!" I cried.

An avalanche, a mountain slide of pistols, of revolvers
fat and bulgeous, of snaky long black automatics, of glit-
tering silvery twenty-twos with tapering slender snouts,
of wicked little pocket guns, slewed and spewed all over
the pavement of Bay St.

Screams and feet pounding, muffled ejaculations and
squeaks, such words as "hold up," "duck" and "Oh my"
filled the air. Car horns, street car bells and racing engines. Big Ben booming, and a flying maelstrom of nine
o'clock figures rushing both ways and across, all crowded
into one cataclysmic instant as Jim seized my elbow; and
head down into the throng, weaving and twisting, we
raced around the corner and into a fish store.

Through its broad windows, we saw the nine o'clock
throng all hasting, with never a sideways glance.

The fish store was abuzz with opening. A man in a
white smock came up.

"A pound of smelts," said Jim.

We caught our breath. We shook hands solemnly. The
smelts were parcelled and paid for.

With chins up and expressions of Torontoesque innocence on our faces, we stepped out into Queen St. and
went the other way around the block.

"Well," I said, "we're rid of the blame things."

"The cops have them by now, I guess," said Jim.

"They're confiscated," I pointed out.

"Isn't it funny how guilty we Toronto people can feel,
even when doing a perfectly legal thing," said Jim.

Which certainly is a curious thing about us.

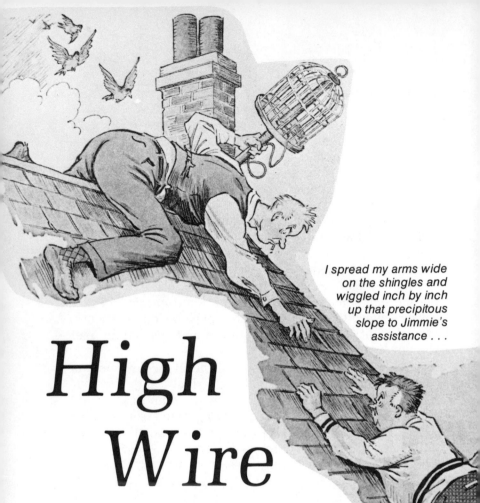

I spread my arms wide on the shingles and wiggled inch by inch up that precipitous slope to Jimmie's assistance . . .

High Wire

April 6, 1935

"My radio," said Jimmie Frise, "is on the bum."

"The same here," I said. "Last night I couldn't get anything but sopranos and dramas."

"I mean," said Jimmie, "mine won't work. It hisses and squawks and when you do get a program, it throbs and wavers."

"You should have heard the soprano I had on last night," I agreed. "Talk about throbbing and squawking."

"What I mean is," persisted Jim, "there is something mechanical wrong with mine."

"Don't be too sure," I argued. "Even if you buy a new one, you'll get sopranos that hiss and squeal worse than if your tubes were worn out. And dramas—there are certain hours, nowadays, where you can twist right around the dial and find nothing but dramas, tense-voiced men and terrified women. My idea is that we radio listeners should be able, at all times, to get what we want on the radio."

"Oh, is that so?" said Jim.

"Certainly it's so," I said heatedly. "Why shouldn't it be?"

"Did it never occur to you," demanded Jim, "that the people who put on that free entertainment are doing a rather magnificent thing for us?"

"Free?" I shouted. "Do you call it free entertainment when I pay $300 for the machine that allows those guys to shove their commercial advertisements right into the sanctity of my home?"

"Er-ah," said Jim.

"Er-ah, exactly," I said. "You are like a lot of other people. You sit down with a sappy grin and listen thankfully while hundreds of commercial enterprises come and yell at you."

"But some of those advertisers," pointed out Jimmie, "pay as much as $10,000 for a half-hour program."

"Why shouldn't they," I inquired, "when there are potentially 1,000,000 listeners? We shouldn't have to listen to baloney. There should be a law against baloney."

"You could easily turn it off if you don't like it," explained Jim.

"Why should I have to get up, in my own home," I shouted, "and turn off my own machine because some public nuisance is allowed on the air?"

171

"I never heard that argument before," admitted Jim.

"Well," I said, "there are too many sopranos and too many dramas on the air. And too many public speakers. And too many comedians. And too many gabblers. Gabble, gabble, gabble. Do you know, there is a fortune waiting for the announcer who will speak in a slow, dreamy voice? The way some of those announcers talk, you'd think they were describing a hotel fire."

A Kind of Electric Scum

"Well, even so, I wish my radio was working right," said Jim. "There are enough lovely programs to make it worthwhile."

"Sure there are," I agreed. "There is the Booka Boola hour. They don't even announce the program. They just start a vast, heavenly orchestra and a more than heavenly choir. And for half an hour, without a single yammering, stuttering human voice to spoil it, they fill your house with ecstasy."

"And the symphonies on Sunday," said Jim.

"You can always turn off the commentator," I admitted, "the guy who needs to clear his throat. He's got me coughing so hard by the time his turn is over, I can't hear the rest of the program. Curious about commentators, isn't it? They've all got a bad cold."

"I think it's my tubes," said Jim. "Although I got a new set just before Christmas."

"Maybe it's your aerial," I said.

"I haven't got an aerial," said Jim.

"What?" I cried. "No aerial? How do you expect to catch the music out of the air without an aerial?"

"Lots of people haven't got aerials," affirmed Jim.

"Nonsense, my dear boy," I assured him. "You've simply got to have an aerial. Don't you understand the first principles of radio? Don't you appreciate the simplest everyday facts of radio?"

"I do not," confessed Jim.

"The ether," I showed him, "is full of waves. Not little waves like on Lake Ontario or even on the Atlantic ocean. But great big waves, as you can understand, seeing how big nothing is as compared with something. See?"

"Certainly," said Jim.

"So these colossal waves go waving along, sometimes more than other times; for instance, when there is a storm, the waves are rough, as you can see from your radio. In bad weather, it is harder to catch the music with your aerial than in nice smooth weather."

"I always understood," interrupted Jim, "that radio was instantaneous. That we heard the music at the same instant it was heard in the studio away off in New York or London."

"That just goes to show you," I said, "how fast those ether waves are. But they have to be fast. They have to travel from here to the moon, to the sun, to the farthest star. And naturally, if a wave has to travel that far, it has got to be moving. That is, if it wants to get there in any sort of time at all. If the ether waves were slow, they might get so tired going a billion miles that they would lose interest altogether in where they were going. So you see the scientific principle there? They have a long way to go. So naturally, they go fast."

"I think I follow you," said Jim.

"Anyway, there on the top of that illimitable sea of ether, with gigantic waves flowing away in all directions, floats a sort of wreckage, a sort of flotsam and jetsam, of squeaks, squeals, moans, groans, words, notes, howls, yowls, bawls, squalls."

"I can see it," said Jim, closing his eyes. "A sort of scum."

"A kind of electric scum," I corrected, "to put it scientifically. You have to understand the science of physics these days, Jim. And this is where your aerial comes in."

"Ah," said Jim.

"You stick your aerial up into the air," I demonstrated, "and it has, as you may have noticed, a kind of fish net or trap of wires on it. It catches that scum. That floating wreckage from a thousand ships. And down the wire into your house comes that stuff you catch in your aerial trap."

"Mmmmm," agreed Jim. "But how do you select only certain wreckage from all that must get tangled in your aerial?"

"That is done," I said, "by the dials. That would be too technical for a beginner like you to understand. But you can see how important it is to have an aerial. My dear chap, without an aerial, you can't expect to trap anything. No wonder you have been getting nothing."

"I wonder how much it costs to put up an aerial?" Jim mused.

"Don't be absurd," I said. "You can put up the aerial yourself. Just get some wire and make a sort of bird cage out of it."

"I have an old bird cage down cellar," said Jim.

"Perfect," I assured him. "Nail the bird cage on to a clothes prop, fasten a wire that will run to the ground, and nail the pole to the roof. Simple."

"Lend me a hand?" asked Jim.

"Sure," said I.

So we arranged to attend to the matter before supper, when we would still have daylight. It was only a matter of a few minutes to fasten the old bird cage on to a clothes prop and to attach to it the end of a long piece of telephone wire that would run down and in Jimmie's side window. Jim borrowed ladders from a neighbor and we set them up to the roof.

"Which end will you carry?" asked Jim.

"You don't need me up there," I smiled.

"Of course I do," cried Jim. "It's the only place I do need you."

"Oh, I'm sorry, Jim, but I get the jimjams up any heights. You know that."

"Listen, you're on a roof. A big broad roof. Don't be silly, I can't hold it and nail it, both."

"Absolutely no, Jim," I assured him. "I get dizzy even hanging pictures."

"What did I ask you to help me for?" cried Jim. "Was it to help me nail this thing in the cellar?"

"You'll need somebody to stay on the ground and tell you if you have it straight up," I pointed out. "I'll do that part."

"Then," said Jim, "I'll have to put it off until I get somebody with enough insides to climb a ladder on to a practically flat roof."

"Being afraid of heights is not a matter of insides," I protested. "It has to do with deep and hidden complexes. It is due . . ."

"Never mind," said Jim, starting back to the cellar door.

"All right, then, I said. "I'll help. I'll take the lower end. You go first."

Alone On the Ridge

So Jim went up the ladder first, hoisting the bird cage end of the pole, and I followed, bearing the heavy or bottom end of the pole. Jim went carefully. So did I. Jim got to the roof.

"Wait till I take off my boots," he called down, "Hold everything."

"You'll catch cold," I warned, for the evening was growing dark and chill. Jim's boots passed me going down. Then I saw his legs vanish slowly over the edge of the roof. Only his hands showing, he hoisted the pole, and I lifted.

"Hold steady," said Jim quietly, when I came to the top. He was sprawled out. What had looked like a big flat roof was now a steep and precipitous cliff.

"I'll stay here," I said, clutching the rungs and hooking my feet.

"Take off your boots," said Jim, "it's easy then, in your sock feet."

"Never," I assured him. "Just never."

Jim shoved the pole and cage ahead of him, and with arms and legs spread wide, hinched himself up that awful eerie slope.

I closed my eyes and just hung tight.

"All right," called Jim. "Come along."

When I opened my eyes, Jim was sitting straddle the roof peak, holding the pole upright beside the chimney.

"Come and hold it while I nail it here," said Jim unsteadily.

"Jim, I'm sorry," I said. "It couldn't be done."

Jim stared grimly at me in the twilight. The air was growing colder. Grimly, he stared.

"So," he said, "my old friend, my dear old friend, gets me straddled up here and leaves me flat."

I hooked one leg through the rungs. I slowly untied my laces. I heard my boots drop sickeningly to the distant earth.

I spread my arms wide on the shingles. I inched myself forward, my sock feet clinging pathetically to the last rungs. I thought of the war. I remembered crawling like this, so flat, across dark hushed fields, and I wished I was back at the war again, in No Man's Land, out from Mericourt. It was better there.

I felt Jim's grip on my arm. I got up straddled beside him. I held the pole. Jim nailed and hammered. He wound wire around the chimney.

"Now," he said, "wait here until I go down and attach the wire to the radio, to see if we have the connections right."

"It'll be all right, Jim," I said. "Let's both go down together."

"Wait," said Jim, already leeching his way down the slope. "I'll holler as soon as I find it's working."

"Don't be long," I called, as his head vanished over the edge.

I sat astride the ridge. The darkness was settling. The houses far below me across the street were all warmly lighted.

The Roof Gets Steeper

Suddenly, up the chimney, through the house, out the windows of Jim's house, I heard a great orchestral boom. The radio was working. Working immensely. The house seemed to tremble, to vibrate with it.

"Ah," I said, clearing my throat and getting ready to make the descent. I would call Jim up on some pretext, so that he would be standing at the top of the ladder to receive me.

I heard the program change. I heard it loud and then soft; I heard men's voices jabbering fiercely in the

176

supper-time children's hour.

"Hey," I roared.

A man passing quickly on the street, homeward bent, paused and looked all around him. Then hurried on.

Down the chimney, I roared: "Hey, hey."

And in the Frise house, the tumult and thunder of a radio in good working order filtered through cracks and windows and walls and chimney. It was dark.

"Hey," I bellowed, covering my sock feet with my coat tails.

I thought of taking my penknife and throwing it at a window of a neighboring house. But there were no windows near enough. I watched for passing pedestrians, but everybody in Jimmie's district comes home by car. A dog went by. I yelled at him. He just ran.

"Help, Help, HAAAALP," I let go.

I drummed with my heels on Jim's roof. But all I heard was a constantly shifting faint series of programs, as Jimmie and all his family tried out the beautiful radio.

And every single minute that passed, that vanishing roof grew steeper.

"I—I don't even know exactly where the ladder end is," I quavered to myself. "Oh, haaaaaalllp."

Then I solved it. I reached out and caught the aerial wire. I gave it a sharp yank. It parted.

I waited.

"Hello, up there," came Jimmie's voice from the backyard.

"Come up," I said, "something has happened to the aerial."

Jim came up. I saw his head emerge over the edge.

"Wait there," I said. And down the slope I crabbed, my feet feeling for him.

"It suddenly faded," said Jim.

"The wind shifted the pole," I said. "I think the wire parted."

So while I went down the ladder Jim removed his boots and clawed up to the bird cage.

"Physics," I said to him, as he came down and joined me at the foot of the ladder, "is a thing everybody ought to know a little about in these days."

177

Boom, Boom!

April 27, 1935

*Up the block we marched, Jim
pretending to blow the fife, and the
drum making magnificent thunder . . .*

"Listen," cried Jimmie Frise. "I hear a band."

We stopped the car. In the distance, the music of drums and horns beat on the night air. We were on Yonge St. near King.

"It'll be one of the regiments," said Jim, opening the car window. "What do you say if we park here and stand on the curb to see them go by."

"Maybe it might be the Highlanders," I exclaimed.

"I haven't seen a parade for years," agreed Jim.

So we got out and walked up towards Adelaide St. and picked a nice open space for ourselves, where the bright shop lights glowed out on to the street. Here we would see the soldiers striding by.

The band grew nearer. Along King St. they came and then, with their brass and their buttons agleaming, their white shells or tunics glowing, the Highlanders wheeled up Yonge St. to the magnificent echoing thunder of their great brass band.

Far out in front marched the giant and handsome master of ceremonies, or whatever you call him. Being only a war-time soldier, I don't remember, and perhaps never did know, the technical terms of the military art. But this remarkable specimen of manhood who strode at the head of the Highlanders was enough to make skyscrapers and handsome department stores curl up with envy. Even men held their breath when he went by. And as for the ladies . . .!

Respectfully in rear of him came the band.

With those little mincing steps of the Highlanders, the white spats tapping like a vast ballet, a corps of a thousand dancers, the band and the regiment followed. Nobody on earth walks as proudly as a Scot, or at any rate, an Irishman or Englishman or a Canadian by the name of Smith or Kelly in a Scottish kilt.

"Ah," sighed Jimmie. "Did you ever see anything so inspiring?"

"Let's walk alongside of them," I suggested.

So Jimmie and I joined the pavement walkers who kept abreast of the straight-looking soldiers. We got level with the band. And the Kiltie with the big brass drum, with the leopard skin across his shoulders, thumped with all his might.

"In the next war," I shouted to Jim, "I'm going to play the drum."

"Majors don't play drums," retorted Jim. "You can't have all the fun."

"I would rather play the drum," I said, "than capture Quebec."

"They'd only give a kettle-drum to a little guy like you," pointed out Jim.

"A bass drum would look all the basser," I argued, "on a little man."

With music crashing and clashing up amidst the tall buildings, with legs moving like the legs of a centipede, the Highland regiment crossed Queen St. while traffic stood still and a great throng stood enviously, the young men on the side lines trying to look superior to all this, the young girls clinging to the young men's arms clinging a little less closely for the moment.

"One Drum and They're Done"

"I'm puffed," I said, "let's stand now and watch them."

And so we watched them until the last Scottie stamped truly past and the music was growing dim in the distance.

"But the drum you can hear, long after the horns are gone," Jim noted.

We walked back to the car.

"You can understand," said Jimmie, "how men go to war when you see a regiment go by. It seems to steal your common sense away. I bet if war was declared, one drum up the streets and away they'd all go."

"I wouldn't be too sure," I mused. "A great many of the young men to-day have serious opinions about war. I've talked to the ones in their twenties down at the office. It is about the only serious thought they have."

"One drum and they're done," argued Jim.

"Yet would you willingly send another generation to go through what we went through?" I demanded. "Filthy, futile and without a single gain to be credited to it. War is insane."

"We had some fun," pointed out Jim.

"If another war came," I said, "I would lead a non-co-operation movement, like Gandhi. I would probably go to jail."

"One drum," said Jim, "and you'd be sitting on a horse, roaring."

"No," I corrected. "I would lead a great youth movement, enlisting the young men of Canada in a pacifist league. And once it was well organized, I would hand it over to younger fellows and then I would sneak away and join some regiment overseas. That's what I would do. I would then satisfy both of my principles."

"So you have two principles?" asked Jim.

"Certainly," I assured him. "I am against war. I think war is a crime. But at the same time, like much crime, war is lots of fun. I'd hate to miss it myself, although I would willingly die to spare other men having to go to war."

"You certainly are confused," said Jim.

"So is nearly everybody else," I said. "Most men feel just the way I do."

"Are you a member of any anti-war society?" inquired Jim. "The League of Nations Association or anything?"

"No," I admitted. "They don't attract me. They aren't militant enough to attract men, somehow. A peace organization should be full of war. It should have something to fight for."

"That's queer," agreed Jim.

"If you try to get young men into a society for peace," I went on, "it has a negative appeal. What you want is a positive appeal. Now, for instance, I might start a society for young men called the League of Youth for Making Munitions Only."

"Ah," said Jim.

"This society," I expounded, "would attract hundreds of thousands of young men who would be sworn to make munitions at $15 a day, but who are vowed never to go to war."
181

"Fifteen dollars a day," said Jim.

"That would be the wages," I said. "Same as the last war. The youth of Canada would be willing to do the same for this country as the old men, the politicians, the bankers and big business men. They would gladly sacrifice their time and energy at making money out of munitions. But they would not go to war. They would die first. How's that?"

"Your idea has a lot of points," admitted Jimmie.

"The League of Youth for Making Munitions Only," I repeated, "is now formed. No wealthy old schemer can complain if the youth of the nation are filled with the same patriotism as his. All across Canada, we will have branch societies, organized and trained, so that at a moment's notice, they can spring to the machines and get the munitions pouring out. The weekly meetings of the branches of the League could be devoted to training on lathes and machine shop technique. There will be lectures on the great munition makers of the past; biographical lectures, telling how many millions they made and what they did with them. Mind you, Jimmie, munitions doesn't merely mean shells and guns. It includes wool and blankets and uniforms; food, such as flour and bacon; leather for boots and equipment. There will be room for every kind of young man in our great league. Tradesmen, merchants, clerks, young executives. Room for everybody in the League of Youth for Making Munitions Only."

"I have an idea," contributed Jim. "I'll give it to the world as a gift. It is the Sinkable Battleship. This invention satisfies everybody. We all admit that building battleships is one of the best ways in the world for the big industrialists to make a few million dollars. It also employs thousands of men. And at the same time there are a certain number of valiant young men whose greatest dream is to die violently, to be blown up. Now, this Sinkable Battleship of mine requires no war. In each ship, as it is launched, is hidden a secret bomb, a very powerful bomb, to which is attached a mechanism that will set it off at a certain unknown time, within six months or six years."

"Jimmie," I cried. "How perfect!"

"Yes," admitted Jim. "Therefore, as these battleships rush about the seven seas, at a certain time, unknown to any man living, the battleship will blow up with a terrific bang, all lives will be lost. And right away, the government that owned the ship can place a new order with the big industrialists. More millions can be made by these great shots. More thousands of men can be employed. And another ship's company of valiant young men who want to die can be enlisted. Everybody will be satisfied."

"And all," I rejoiced, "without war being declared at all!"

"Precisely," said Jim. "Every government, even Switzerland, can then have the benefits of war without its evils. It is a remarkable invention, this Sinkable Battleship."

"If we announce my new league in the ordinary way," I said, as we drove slowly along the lovely lake shore, "it will only attract a few of those pimply-faced young men with untidy hair who join leagues. We ought to use our newspaper instincts, Jim. We ought to start it off some exciting way. It ought to be started with a bang."

"With a drum," suggested Jim.

"Exactly," I cried. "Why not? Why let war have all the drums? That's what's the matter with these peace societies. They have no drums."

"I could get you a drum," said Jim. "I know an Orangeman."

"A bass drum?" I asked.

"A big bass drum," assured Jim.

And that is how the League of Youth for Making Munitions Only got started.

Jim's friend tuned the big drum for him, tightening the steel bands around it. He lent Jim a fife too, as Jimmie wanted to have some share in this great movement.

We drove down to University Ave.

"You can always get a following down around Queen and University," I told him. "If you can't get soldiers, you can get Communists. There is always somebody wanting to follow a drum down there."

But when we parked the car, it looked a little forbidding. There were men scattered all along the curbs in the early spring evening. There were men wandering in twos and threes, or stopped chatting.

"Let's start on a side street," I said, "and by the time we have a good following, we can debouch on to the main streets. When we have about a thousand following us, we can halt, I'll jump up on the steps of a monument or something and address them."

We parked in one of those side streets between Elizabeth and University, where Chinese children were playing and foreign ladies were walking along with live fish wriggling violently in loose parcels of newspaper.

I got the drum out. Jim blew through the fife to get the dust out.

"Ready?" said Jim nervously.

We stood side by side.

"Ready, one, two, three," I replied.

Boom, boom, boom.

Up Elizabeth St. we started. Jim can't play a fife. No noise came from it. But it looked good. He wiggled his fingers. He held his head back.

"Don't go too far up or you'll disturb the sick people in the hospital," shouted Jim.

"Correct," I said. "Left wheel!"

We wheeled down Elizabeth St. again. Little Chinese boys lined the curb, and old gentlemen with large beards stuck their heads out of the doors of little frame shops.

"Hallelujah," yelled a colored gentleman, rushing out of a house.

Boom, boom, boom.

"Don't go too far down," said Jim, "or the detectives in the city hall will hear you."

"Left wheel!" I commanded.

The drum was heavy, but what is more important is the fact that a drum vibrates as you hit it. The louder you hit, the livelier it vibrates. And as you are supporting the drum with your abdomen, your abdomen takes the vibration, as it were.

"How many following?" I shouted to Jim, looking out from behind the drum.

"Nobody yet," said Jim. "Hit it louder."

Some foreign ladies with live fish wriggling in newspapers gathered on the curb with the children. Several of the bearded men came and sat on the steps to await what was to happen.

"Left wheel!" commanded Jim.

Up and down the block we marched, Jim pretending fiercely to blow the fife and the drum making a magnificent thunder.

Then a bearded man in a striped apron and wearing a derby hat ran out with his hand held high.

"Stop, stop," he cried. We stopped.

"You wake all the babies," he said.

"Sir," I replied, "we are awaking the entire youth of the nation, perhaps of the world."

"Would you please wake them on another street?" asked the bearded man, lifting his derby politely.

"That's a reasonable request," Jimmie said.

"All right," I agreed. "This drum is heavier than I expected."

So we went down and got in the car.

We put the drum in. Through the car windows, I looked back up the street. All was quiet. Little Chinese children played on the darkening pavement. The bearded men had got up and gone back into their shops. The ladies with the parcels were pursuing their patient way. It was as if no drum had beaten.

Down Elizabeth St., a slow pacing policeman came to a halt at the distant corner and stood looking up street.

"Peaceful, isn't it?" said Jim.

The doors of the armories, south of us, swung hugely open.

There was a sudden thunder of drums. A sudden scream of bugles. Out of the door marched the first ranks of a regiment. A very tall man leading. He was ceremoniously waving an immense gold-knobbed baton.

The policeman leaped to life. He took the centre of the street, stopping traffic with majestic arm.

"Let's follow them," said Jim, stepping on the starter.

So we followed the regiment around nine blocks.

Strategy

June 8, 1935

The big man was hurling handfuls of sod a the little old bailiff . .

"The nerve," said Jimmie Frise, "of some people."

We had just passed a rather cheesy-looking individual on the highway, who thumbed us most imperatively as we sailed by.

"He looked," I admitted, "as if you might get bugs from him."

"Why a raggedy-looking specimen like that," said Jim, "should expect a lift is more than I can understand. I don't mind giving a lift to a respectable-looking person, but some of the hikers who thumb most commandingly should hardly expect to be allowed in at a dog fight."

"Maybe we could write something," I suggested, "that would suggest to hikers that they clean themselves up. Let's tip off the hiking fraternity that the ratio of the lifts they get is in exact proportion to their clean and tidy appearance."

"Not a bad idea," said Jim. "Yet I'm a little leery of those too tidy ones. Last week, I gave a lift to a very polished gentleman along by Port Hope, and he wondered if I wouldn't be so kind as to run him up a few miles north of the highway to some forsaken little dump he mentioned."

"The nerve!"

"Yes," said Jimmie, "and when I refused, he got out of my car with all the outraged airs of a bank president who couldn't get front row seats at the box office."

"This whole business of hitch hikers is a queer one," I related. "I know a chap who was signalled by a nice-looking girl on the highway out near Oakville. She stepped right out in front of the car and he had to stop. She was in a hurry to get to Toronto. So he took her aboard. Just as they came over the Humber bridge, the girl suddenly tore her blouse and rumpled her hair, and started to scream. My friend slowed down in fright and astonish-

186

ment. 'Now,' says the nice young lady, 'there's a cop at
the far end of the bridge. You come across with $5 or I'll
lean out and scream at him, and what a nice mess you'll
be in!' "

"Good grief!" gasped Jimmie. "What did he do?"

"He did the only sensible thing," I delighted to tell
him. "He drove straight to the cop, and said, 'Here's a
young lady who signalled me for a ride out the highway,
and now she has torn her dress and said she'd scream to
you if I didn't hand her over $5.' And the cop said, 'Good,
we've been on the watch for this jane for three weeks,' so
they all drove up to the police station."

"Boy," breathed Jim, "I wouldn't know what to do in a
jam like that."

"I knew another chap who picked up a young man and

a girl," I told Jim, "and they said they were going to Oril-lia. My friend was going to Gravenhurst so he said hop in. When they were passing one of those swamps beyond Barrie, the girl, who said she had once lived on a farm near there, told about a wonderful cold spring that bub-bled out of the earth right near the road. The coldest, loveliest water you ever tasted."

"I see what's coming," said Jim.

"So," I related, "they stopped by the road and every-body got out and went into the cedar swamp. And the girl led the way into the thicket and said it's right around here somewhere, so they scattered out to look, when my friend heard his car start."

"Holy," said Jim.

"So by the time my friend got out to the pavement," I concluded, "there was his car vanishing up the road at sixty miles an hour. He flagged a lift and gave chase, but the car had disappeared. You can't expect the first guy you beg a lift off to hit sixty. He got the police at Orillia to help him. But the next he saw his car, it was in Goderich, with a seized engine, and all his property gone out of it, and old tires on it in place of the good tires."

"Well I never," confessed Jimmie.

"The great thing is," I stated, "don't pick anybody up. It is better to be a meanie a thousand times than to try to explain something to your wife even once."

"I suppose so," agreed Jim. "There is enough trouble in this world, dealing only with your immediate friends and relatives, without getting yourself tangled up with strangers."

We drove along in philosophic silence.

"Yet it seems a pity," pursued Jim, "that a thousand deserving people, with sore feet and weary hearts, should have to be left standing on the side of the road all for the fear of the one scoundrel."

"You can pretty well tell," I said, "what a man is like from the outside. Men, for the most part, are pretty sim-ple and straight-forward. Most men are not schemers."

"I hate schemers," declared Jim. "But I pride myself on the fact that I can smell a schemer a mile off. I can tell by their eyes. They have an honest, wide-eyed sort of look. They look you right in the eye."

"I thought it was the other way around," I exclaimed. "I thought schemers were shifty-eyed and never could meet your gaze."

"That's a lot of stuff you read in novels," said Jim. "Just think of your friends. Think of the most honest of them all. Is he wide-eyed and innocent?"

I thought for a moment.

"No, by George," I admitted, "now that you mention it, he has a shy and shifty glance. I never noticed that before."

"It's always the way," pointed out Jim. "Human nature, at its best, is shy and timid and kindly and uncertain. But the boys who are certain and bold and crafty, they are the ones who look you bung in the eye."

"Well, sir, that's news to me," I agreed.

Ahead of us, far up Yonge street, as we zoomed along for Lake Simcoe, we saw a figure of a man hobbling painfully on a stick.

As we neared him, we saw that he was elderly and bowed, and his foot was done up in a bandage. He was barely able to hobble.

"Poor chap," said Jim. "I wonder if he has far to go?"

"This is an exception," I admitted. "We couldn't really pass him by."

Jimmie was already slackening the car. We drew up ahead of the poor old chap, and as we did so, his face lighted up with pleased surprise and he hastened as fast as his bandaged foot would let him.

"Have you far to go?" called Jim, as I opened the car door.

"Just a little way," cried the old man anxiously. "Up two cross roads, and then in one concession."

"We can't see you hobbling along like that," said Jim.

"It's a mighty sore foot," said the old chap. "But of course I wouldn't expect you to drive me right in. Just you gentlemen leave me on the corner, and somebody will come along sooner or later and take me in."

"Not at all, not at all," assured Jim. "We've nothing to do. We're just going fishing. It won't be ten minutes out of our way."

The old chap's face was a delight to behold, at this information.

"You'll take me right to the door?" he exclaimed. "Well, now, I call that mighty fine of you gentlemen. You don't find many folks that way these days."

He got in the back seat and made himself comfortable. I noticed how wide and innocent and blue his eyes were. He had a candid gaze, if ever a man did. But I realized that in the country they have a more gentle and innocent outlook on life than we city slickers. They don't have to be so crafty in the country.

"Two roads up," said Jim, as he got the car booming along again.

"Two roads up, and then turn right, and it's just near the end of the concession," said the old chap. "My, this is nice of you. And what a nice big car you've got."

"We couldn't very well pass a man of your age, struggling along the way you were going," admitted Jim. "Did you hurt your foot?"

"No, it isn't exactly hurt," contributed the old chap. "It's a kind of sciaticky or arthritis or something. It catches me something terrible. And then all of a sudden it leaves me."

"It isn't gout?" asked Jim.

"No, not gout," said the old chap. "I hardly ever took a drink in my life, scarcely. I think it's what we used to call the rheumatics. But it's an awful painful thing."

Delivering a Blue Paper

"It must be bad getting around, if you're a farmer," suggested Jim.

"I'm not exactly a farmer," said the old chap. I turned to face him and I noticed how clear and guileless his eyes were. I thought of Gray's Elegy and honest plowmen and all sorts of things. "No, I ain't a farmer, exactly, although I have done farming."

"What is your business?" asked Jim.

"Well, I'm kind of an official," said the old chap. proudly. "I'm a kind of sherrif's man, a kind of bailiff, so to speak."

"You ought to have plenty to do these days," laughed Jimmie over his shoulder. "Throwing people off their farms and that sort of thing."

"Oh, yes, I get some fun," said the old chap.

"Is this the turn?" called Jim.

"Yes, this is it," said the bailiff. "Now, if you feel you can't waste the time . . ."

"Nonesense," cried Jim. "It won't take us five minutes. One concession over?"

"One concession," agreed the old fellow.

So we turned east and swung along a nice gravel road, passing farms on right and left.

"You live in here?" asked Jim.

"No," said the bailiff, "I'm just delivering a paper in here. If it wouldn't put you out any, I thought, maybe, while you are turning your car around, you might wait until I deliver the paper, and then I could get a lift back out to the road . . ."

"Certainly, certainly," said Jim, but he gave me a look just the same.

"You gentlemen certainly are very kind," said the bailiff. "I hope some day I can return you the favor."

"It's quite all right," said Jim. "You won't be long?"

"The next lane," said the old fellow. "Just run up the next lane. You can see a farm house from here, see? And while you turn the car around I can just pop this document in and be right aboard again."

He seemed a little breathless. His wide innocent eyes were shining with suppressed excitement.

Up the lane we ran, and into a farmyard in the midst of which stood a tidy house. But it had a sort of fortified look, if I make myself clear. There were no implements nor buck saws leaning about, not even a chair on the front porch. The blinds were down.

"Everybody away?" I said.

"No, he'll be in all right," said the old gentleman, as we drew up alongside the back door. He was shaking with excitement. He opened the car door quickly and hopped out, at the same time drawing a large blue paper from his pocket.

Jim started to turn the car. The old chap, whose sciaticky seemed much improved, skipped to the door and rapped loudly. The door opened, and as we were busy backing the car and turning it, I saw a huge man in overalls, with stubble all over his chin, looking fiercely out of the crack of the door down at the little man who was holding out the blue paper.

As we completed the turn in the yard and started to back up to the door again for our passenger, we were both astonished to see him running wildly down the lane past us, with no trace of sciaticky at all in his foot, and behind him, taking large jumps and stooping to pick up handfuls of sod and gravel, the big man was bounding, shouting angrily and hurling the divots at the back of the neck of the little old man.

"Here, here," said Jim, starting the engine. But the big chap was returning towards him with giant strides. We stopped.

The big fellow reached in and took Jimmie by the scruff of his necktie shirt front.

"So," he said, "you're a couple of professional bullies, eh? Who's the little man, eh? Would it be Jack Dempsey, maybe?"

And before I could say a word, he reached past Jimmie and, seizing the brim of my hat, yanked it down over my nose.

"Keep out of here," roared the big man, giving Jim's head an awful waggle with that grip he had of Jim's tie. "Don't stick your snoot around here, if you don't want to be kicked over that there barn."

"Yes, sir," said I.

Jim started the car. Down the lane it rocked, and made the turn. Far away, just vanishing over a rise in the road we saw the bailiff. He was making time any school boy would envy.

"I'll run over him," grated Jim, slamming into high gear.

As we came near, the bailiff jumped into the grassy ditch. The bandage on his foot had come loose and was trailing. His face was flushed and he seemed to be laughing.

"Would you mind," shouted Jim, "explaining what this is all about?"

"It's all right, it's all right," assured the little man, with anxious looks down the road. "I was serving eviction papers on him."

"And what's this about us being prize-fighters?" inquired Jimmie icily.

"Oh, I just told him for fun that I had a couple of hired prize-fighters along with me in the car," deprecated the little old man.

"He nearly strangled me," declared Jim, "with my own necktie."

"He pulled my hat over my eyes," I added indignantly.

"He didn't catch me," said the old bailiff, proudly.

"By the way, what about that sore foot?" demanded Jim. "You were hardly able to walk when we first saw you fifteen minutes ago."

"Oh, just one of those things a bailiff has to think of," said he, stooping to unwind the bandages. "I couldn't get any of the local boys to come with me. They wouldn't even come in a car. They wouldn't even come as far as the lane, and wait down on the road. No, sir. I couldn't get anybody in the whole township to come with me to serve those papers. So I just had to use strategy. I had six cars stop before you came along, but I wanted the right car, and that was you."

"Strategy," sneered Jim. "Strategy, a dirty trick, I call it."

"If you were a bailiff," said the old chap, his rosy face bright with indignation, "you wouldn't call it a dirty trick to try to get somebody to come with you to serve eviction papers on a man like that."

In the distance, we heard buggy wheels flying on gravel.

"Hey," gasped the little old man, scrambling toward us.

But Jim just slammed her into gear and away.

"Strategy," he yelled back.

And we never waited to see whether he caught him or not.

"Here he is," announced Patrick, as a Chinese appeared in the doorway, smiling uncertainly . . .

Come Illy Bong

June 29, 1935

"Ah," cried Jimmie Frise, "come illy bong!"

"Come what?" I requested anxiously.

"Come illy bong." explained Jimmie. "It's a French saying. It means, 'Ah, how good it is'."

"How good what is?" I asked.

"Everything," cried Jim, expanding his chest and sighing. "This June day. This new flannel suit I've got on. This blue tie. This crisp, fresh underwear. I feel like a million dollars."

"I'm glad you feel good," I said. "I feel kind of dowdy myself."

"Ah," sighed Jim. "To feel good all the time. To feel fresh and crisp and cool and listless, if you get me?"

"I think so," I said doubtfully.

"I mean, life could be so swell," said Jim tenderly. "If only we could surround ourselves with the finer things, good clothes, nice furniture, pleasant people. Just to hold this feeling I have right now and hold it all my life!"

"Maybe it would be kind of monotonous," I suggested.

"I think," said Jim thoughtfully, "that this feeling I have right now, this sense of well-being, this cleanness and peacefulness, is the goal of all human life. I think this is what millionaires and kings and princes, all those swell people you read about in England and Boston and the Riviera are aiming at. What you call culture. Culture is the business of getting hold of this feeling I have right now and making it permanent."

"Some days it would be rainy," I suggested.

"Do you ever read those society magazines?" asked Jim. "They sometimes show two or three pages of somebody's estate. Beautiful big gardens all filled with flagstone walks and statues and fountains."

"And nobody in them," I pointed out.

"And big cool houses," went on Jim, "and rooms filled with only a little bit of furniture, but all of it old and antique and oval and lovely."

"The chairs look as if nobody had ever sat in them," I remarked.

"And grand staircases," continued Jim. "Great curving walnut staircases. And panelled walls with maybe two paintings."

"I've seen them," I agreed. "The living quarters are in the attic."

"I'm trying to explain something," said Jim, "if you'd give me a chance. What I mean is that sense of peace and purity you see in those estates. That's culture. That's the way these rich people try to seize hold of this feeling I have got to-day and keep it forever. Now, you take food. Do you know what a gourmet is?"

"A guzzler," I said.

"Just the reverse," said Jim. "A gourmet is a person of discrimination in eating. He is a judge of good food. He never eats anything but what is cooked by an artist. He has taste. He wants food prepared for his sense, not to fill him up like pancakes."

"I like waffles," I admitted. "They fill you up."

"Ugh," said Jim, waving his hand delicately. "A gourmet feels the way I do all the time. Only it is his eating that keeps him cool and dreamy and peaceful. He thinks of eating all the time. As soon as he finishes one meal of, say, goose's brains and truffles, which is a kind of mushroom, he lies back and starts thinking up something he will have for supper, say, plover's eggs and filet of sole à la Mornay."

Culture is a Food

"Where did you get all this stuff?" I asked.

"It comes to me naturally," said Jim, "when I feel like this, I think some of my ancestors were French gourmets. The French are the most cultured people on earth."

"Well," I said, "between thinking of those pictures of beautiful estates in the society magazines and thinking of fancy eating, sort of dreamy like, taking little nibbles and rolling your eyes between each taste, I don't think I would care much about being cultured."

"You will observe," said Jim, "that the big game hunters, the African lion hunters, are always rich people and Belgian barons and so forth. That is their occasional reaction. When they get too much culture, they go lion hunting in Africa and eat cornpones cooked by Congo savages."

"Culture," I said, "is all right in its place, but it must be awful as a regular thing. Suppose you wanted to yawn and yell and get up and kick the cuspidor? You couldn't do that if you were cultured."

"The more I think of it," ignored Jim, "the more I realize that we masses . . ."

"Ah," said I.

"We masses are missing the greatest things in life," said Jim, "by not cultivating this inward peace, this feeling of perfection. We toil and slave for some cheap and tawdry goal. We live amidst higgledy-piggledy furniture and eat food that fills us, that's all. If only we could give all mankind a hint of how lovely life can be, every passing hour of life, every day. And have all mankind gently, culturally striving, without effort, to achieve this goal."

"I like that about gently striving, without effort," I admitted. "Sort of dreamily working, like."

"If, instead of the terrible drive of modern life," de-

197

clared Jim, "we could gear life down to a gentle pursuit of a feeling, a sense, a state of mind, even taxi-drivers and steam shovel men could be cultured."

"How would we go about getting cultured?" I asked. "Would we have to go back to the university and all that sort of thing?"

"If you didn't get it at the university the first time," said Jim, "you won't get it the second time. I venture to say that I could give you a better feeling of culture by taking you through an antique store for a couple of hours, and then leisurely wandering into a high-class restaurant where there is a good French chef and ordering a dinner for a gourmet, than five years at the university would give you."

"I'll do that some day," I confessed. "Because the two years I was at the university, there was no talk about culture. A man away off at the far end of a big amphitheatre with 700 students in it shouted something about the corollary of the theorem. That wasn't culture. And going to rugby games and having to yell the way the fellow in the white sweater signalled at us wasn't culture. One time I tried to spend a night wandering amongst those lovely old stone towers on Varsity campus to look at the stars, but Christie, the campus cop, chased me and told me to go home. It was no good."

"Culture," said Jim, "is a feeling, a mood. I'm in it now. Right now, I am cultured. I could go through an antique store right now and appreciate everything, the old glossy wood, the curves of the carving on chairs, the size and proportions of tables and dressers. I could look and fondle old silver. Away back in me something would wake and start to glow, like an ember in a fire that had gone out . . ."

"Jim," I said, "I have a little feeling like that, too. Let's go."

"When one feels this way, one ought to go," admitted Jim, rising elegantly.

"They're My Set-Up"

So we went to a little antique store that Jim knew of because the man who runs it often meets Jim at the races where they choose the same horse. Dim and shadowy was the little store, and filled to the roof with lovely old antique furniture. So dim and shadowy was it, that the furniture seemed more antique than ever.

Old chairs, tables, funny little stands, pictures, old silver, tall cabinets, foot stools. The young lady who was in charge because Jim's friend was away for the afternoon allowed us to wander among. We sat on old sofas, examined old tables and looked at the pegs that held them together instead of nails; fondled old silver teapots the girl brought us reverently; Jim working up tears in his eyes several times, tears of appreciation of something specially fine. Most of all, we liked two chairs and a little table that stood in the window of the store.

They were perfect. The wood seemed to glow from within. The design actually flowed.

We were still admiring these pieces when the boss came in, very dejectedly. He shook Jim's hand sadly. Jim said:

"Not getting them these days, Ernie?"

"To-day," said Ernie, "five of the six ran in the can. And the sixth one paid $1.15."

So they talked horses for a while, and then Jim gradually wooed Ernie off horses and onto antiques. But Ernie was off antiques for good.

"Just like the horses I bet on," he growled.

"We like those two chairs and that table in the window," said Jim.

"You can't have those," said Ernie firmly. "They're my set up."

"Your what?" asked Jim.

"My set up," said Ernie. "I spent eight years in the antique business to get those. They're what bring people in here."

"Naturally," said Jim, "you put your prize pieces in the window. But wouldn't you sell them?"

"Sell those!" exclaimed Ernie indignantly. "They're genuine."

"Er—" said Jimmie, turning to look back in the shadowy store.

"Er—to you," said Ernie. "Do you imagine for one

minute that a gang of hicks working with hand tools a hundred and fifty years ago could make as good antiques as trained men with modern machinery can make? Be yourself, Jimmie."

"But those in the window," I protested.

"Listen," said Ernie, "there were about ten artists a hundred and fifty years ago, and every stick they made is known to the world, just the way every picture Rembrandt painted is known. If you want any good antiques, I can get them made for you better than all the woodchoppers of Queen Anne's reign. And within six days."

"The silver?" said Jim, a little brokenly. "That teapot?"

"Exquisite 1934," said Ernie contemptuously. "Stick to horse racing, Jim."

"That sofa?" said Jim. "Horse hair?"

"My man made it in two days," said Ernie, "Listen, Jim, when that sofa was supposed to be made the mobs of France were burning the chateaux; in England, millions were starving before the Napoleonic wars put up the price of goods, and the world was poverty-stricken in a way you can't even imagine. How many swell homes do you suppose there were in the eighteenth century in order to equip all the swell mansions of the States, Canada, England, France and Germany to-day?"

A Silence As of Watching

Jim took another long look at the lovely dusky furniture, the gleaming silver, the smudgy oil paintings on the walls.

"Well, I'll be seeing you at the races," he said, and we went out.

We drove down the street.

"I've lost the feeling," said Jim. "I feel soggy and damp. But maybe if we could get a little good food, if we could find a chef, a real chef."

"I saw the dearest little place," I told him. "Just a plain little restaurant with small menus in ordinary handwriting on the windows. Let's take a look at it."

Jim followed my directions and we came, just as the crowds were going home, to the restaurant with the small unimposing front, and the menu stuck in the window. We got out of the car and studied the carte du jour.

"Hors d'oeuvres varies
Potage paysanns
Filets de brochet
Poule Rotie
Asperges, petits pois
Pommes de toutes sortes,
Petits fours
Cafe."

"Read that," hissed Jimmie. "See that paysanns? That means peasant. I bet we have here the sort of chef you'd fine in those little lost French towns, where kings and prime ministers go and hide in order to eat the incomparable cooking."

"Not much on the menu, Jim," I cautioned.

"Not much on the outside of the shop, either," snorted Jim, "because, unlike the local beaneries, the value is inside, not outside. Let's go in."

Inside were five tables and one aged waiter in a black coat and white apron, who immediately began flicking around with his serviette when we came in the door. A silence filled the little restaurant. A silence as of watching.

"Good evening," said Jim to the waiter, "what sort of a chef have you here?"

"Best in the country, sir," replied the waiter, with an Irish accent. "Best in the country."

Disillusioned Again

"Where has he been besides here?" asked Jim, still standing up.

"All over, in the foinest places," said the waiter. "He done a long time in Vancouver. He's been in Montreal, Quebec, and many foreign places."

"Foreign places?"

"Sure, foreign places, I couldn't remember the names," said the waiter enthusiastically.

We sat down.

"Start," said Jimmie, "at the top and go right down the menu."

"It's a fifty-cent dinner," warned the waiter.

"Tut, tut," said Jim.

Hors d'oeuvres varies were four olives, two pieces of celery and two radishes.

Potage paysanne was vegetable soup, filets de brochet looked like pike to me, the poule was plain chicken, asperges were asparagus the same as ever, and petits fours were little fancy biscuits with a local factory name printed on them in the baking.

But Jim persuaded me the meal was incomparable.

"Ex-squeezy," he said. "Come illy bong!"

"I've tasted that vegetable soup on camping trips," I whispered. "Out of cans."

"My dear boy, you'll need to take a course," he said. "Your palate is dulled. This fish! Taste it!"

"Pike, I swear," I whispered.

But the old waiter kept coming in and out, so I caught some of Jim's enthusiasm, and by the time we had finished the coffee and fancy biscuits, the old waiter, whose name was Patrick, was practically sitting at the table with us. He seemed lonesome.

"You don't get many people in here," said Jim.

"Just the crème," said Patrick.

"Now, look here," said Jim, "amongst my kind of people, as you know, Patrick, it is a custom when we have enjoyed a meal and recognized the hand of a master in the cooking, we see the chef and pay him our compliments direct."

"Sure, sure," said Patrick.

"Now would you be kind enough to step in there and ask Monsieur to come into the room while we compliment him?"

"Sure, sure," said Patrick, uneasily. "He's a busy man right now. Maybe some other time, when you're dining?"

"Busy?" cried Jim. "Patrick, be so good as to ask Monsieur to step out here a minute."

Patrick got up, waving his serviette hopelessly. He vanished through the kitchen door and was gone quite a long time. Presently the door slowly opened, and in backed Patrick.

"Here he is, gintlemen," said he.

And in a large white hat and an oversize apron, freshly unfolded, appeared a Chinese, smiling uncertainly.

"Ah," said Jim.

"Ha," said Monsieur. "Muchee like?"

"Very nice meal," said Jim, rising. And we both laid a dime down for Patrick. And got our hats. And were rather awkward getting out the door.

In the car, as we went down towards the lake shore for home, Jim said:

"Culture is a bit elusive nowadays."

And he tooted his horn violently at a fat lady scuttling across Dundas Street against the red light.

Four
Bits

November 2, 1935

"What," asked Jimmie Frise, sarcastically, "are you wearing that particular expression for?"

I was driving. We were bowling along Bloor street.

"What expression?" I inquired.

"An expression," stated Jim, "of abject humility. A disgusting, lowly, Uriah Heep expression."

"You saw that speed cop, didn't you?" I demanded.

"Yes, I did," said Jim. "And that is what I am getting at. You are driving along, perfectly natural. Suddenly, you see a speed cop standing on the curb. And you deflate yourself like a toy balloon. You fairly sag with humility. You cringe like a dog. You actually fawned in your seat. You did it so glaringly that the cop couldn't help but see it."

"I intended the cop to see it," I explained. "I did it for him."

"Disgusting," said Jim.

"Disgusting nothing," I retorted. "That is how you don't get summonses."

"Absurd," snorted Jim. "A cop is a hired official. We hire them. They work for us. The way you act, you'd think they were our masters."

"A cop," I expounded, "has a greater sense of majesty

204

The fat man put his foot slap over my fifty cents . . .

than anybody else in the world. No king left on earth has as much sense of personal majesty as a cop."

"What of it?" cried Jim. "I'd take more pleasure in puncturing their sense of majesty than in contributing to it. The way you do."

"Listen, Jim," I begged. "use your common sense. How does a cop select those to whom he will send summonses?"

"Why," exclaimed Jim, "he selects those that speed or otherwise break the law."

"Now it is you who are absurd," I triumphed. "How many people in this city don't break the speed laws every day?"

"Oh, well, I suppose there are a good many that do," admitted Jim.

"A good many!" I cried. "Listen, Jim, the only people who don't go faster than 20 miles an hour in Toronto are those who can't. There is a certain type of wooden-jointed man, the kind of man who has to stop and think for a minute before he even picks up his knife and fork at the dinner table; and there is a certain kind of timid, middle-aged lady; but those are the only people in the city who don't every day, every time they go driving, in short, every block they drive, exceed the speed limit."

"I know. I know," cut in Jim, "but the cops use a little reason. They only pick out the excessive speeders."

"Aha," I derided, "but did you ever get a summons for going thirty-one miles an hour?"

"Oh, yes," agreed Jim.

"Yet you know thousands of your fellow citizens go more than thirty-one every day all around you?"

"Sure," confessed Jim.

"Very well," I inquired, "how did the cop pick on you out of all the thousands that were doing the same thing?"

"Er," said Jim.

Why Does a Cop Pick You?

"Exactly," I stated. "Exactly. He didn't like your looks, that's why he selected you. Every day a cop has to pick up so many people for speeding, see? He has thousands to pick from. Therefore, who does he pick?"

"Er," said Jim.

"I'll tell you," I interrupted. "A cop is a human being, just like us. But he has a sense of majesty. The ones he picks, out of all the pickings, is the one that offends his sense of majesty, first. Or the one that, for some reason or another, he doesn't like the look of."

"This is awful," gasped Jim.

"Sure, it's awful," I agreed. "It puts the whole problem of right and wrong back where it was in the middle ages or in the time of Pontius Pilate."

"How can we escape being selected?" asked Jim.

"By kow-towing," I stated promptly. "By paying reverence to his majesty the cop. By slowing down when you pass him, even if you are only going as fast as all the other cars in the line. That little sudden slow down you do when you see a cop is a salute to him. A genuflexion. It is a bow to his majesty. He can't help but love it. You and me, if we were cops, we'd love it. It would tickle us."

"It wouldn't come very easy to me," said Jim.

"All you have to do is look impressed," I said. "People use the same expression whenever they meet the boss on the street. So what's the difference? They don't mean it then and they don't mean it with the cop. It's just a little social device. Treat a cop with reverence and you'll never get a summons."

"To hell with it," suddenly Jim shouted. "To hell with it. I won't do it. I'll kow-tow to no cop. To nobody. To no bishop or king. To nobody. I won't do it."

"Dear me," I said, for Jim was sitting up straight and glaring about, and I knew full well there would be a cop pretty soon, just along past that rise by High Park.

"What's more," said Jim, "I'm going out of my way to stand erect in the presence of all these artificial majesties. The majesty of wealth, pah!"

"Wait until we get past High Park," I cautioned him.

"Pooie," shouted Jim, "pooie to riches and power and authority. I'll stand on my own two feet. I'll curtsey to no cop."

"Rich men," I said, laughingly, "give me a pain, Jim.

There has always been a trick I'd love to play on rich men. Did I ever tell you about it?"

"Cops," sneered Jim. "Majesty."

"My trick," I said, "is to stand outside some club downtown, one of those rich men's clubs, and hold a fifty-cent piece in my hand. Just as some of these big shots come down the steps of their club and step on to the sidewalk, looking very well fed and important and chatting together, I drop the fifty-cent piece on the pavement behind them."

"And what?" said Jim, a little interested!

"See these big shots wheel as if they had been stung," I crowed, "snatching at their pockets and all poised to make a grab for the coin."

"It would be fun," confessed Jim, somewhat mollified. We were now passing High Park, and the cop wasn't there.

"Let's do it," I said. "For half an hour we could have more fun than a picnic."

Which was the birth of our idea, and the next day, at noon, we hurried lunch and went and stood at a certain club where many wealthy citizens take their midday repast.

It was my fifty cents. A big, new, tingling one. I dropped it a few times, and it made a loud, rousing ring on the pavement.

The Ring of a Coin

I recommend this trick to you. You can make anybody in the world wheel around like a shot. You can make old and young, the deaf, the halt and the blind, millionaires and bums—everybody stop in their tracks and grab for their pockets or purses. All with the merry ring of a coin dropped on the pavement. I wonder if it isn't the saddest fact left in the world today?

We took up our stand, as if we had just met on the street and were chatting about the weather.

The first citizens to emerge from the club were two tall, tweedy-dressed men in their late forties, keen-looking, bronzed, alert. As they turned on to the sidewalk, clink went the coin.

Both wheeled, the shorter one taking a grip on the arm of the other, as if to prevent him from getting there first. With a smile I picked the coin up and, blushing furiously, the two general managers straightened and hastened down the street.

The next was a large and lonely individual, troubled with his feet. He lowered himself down the steps with great care, one step at a time. Groaning and grunting, he reached the sidewalk.

He turned away. I dropped the coin.

"Ah!" gasped the decrepit chairman of the board, slapping both hands to his pockets, and turning with obvious difficulty. His eyes were popping from his head, and his soft mouth was wide open in the expression of one who has been clubbed on the head.

I picked up the coin with a smile. The gentleman stood, staring coldly at me for a long moment, doubtful, suspicious, his wrinkled fingers softly feeling the outside of his pockets.

At last, while Jim and I chatted briskly, he seemed to reach a decision. He turned away and walked down the street. I suppose he entered it in the books as a loss.

The next lot were three youngish men. The next after them, two very severe-faced gentlemen, pale and bony-jawed, their expression one of unrelaxed vigilance. When they die, it will be hard to get their eyes shut. All these wheeled, as everybody wheels. As you and I and Jimmie, as all the world wheels, to the siren jingle of a coin.

"I'm getting a little tired of this," I said. "It makes me want to cry, not laugh."

"Just one more," gloated Jim. "Let's try to knock off at least a president of something. Somebody who is always having his pictures in the papers."

But the next one that came out was another single. He was a short, stoutish gentleman in a bowler hat. He had a walking stick. He moved with short, waddling steps. His face, though round, was all shut up like a nut cracker. His eyes seemed shut. His mouth was tight shut, and walled in between little round pouchy cheeks.

His ears were small and shut up close to his head. Down the steps he trotted briskly, carefully.

I dropped the coin.

The little man, never pausing, wheeled like a polo pony and before I could even start to stoop, down came a large, flat shoe, a shoe with no toe caps, a square toed, well made shoe, slap on top of my fifty-cent piece.

"Pardon me," I said, half stooping.

But the stubby little man himself stooped, carefully slid his boot to one side, until the edge of the coin was visible, and then with a cleverly bent finger, he released it, snapped it up and popped it in his pants pocket.

"Ah," he sighed, comfortably, and started to move off, without even so much as looking at Jim or me. He seemed utterly unaware of us.

To Torment the Rich

"Just a minute, there," said Jim, taking hold of the gentleman's sleeve.

"What do you want?" demanded the gentleman crisply.

"That was my friend's fifty cents," warned Jim, standing close to the gentleman.

"It was nothing of the kind," said the gentleman, not unkindly, but very finally, "I dropped it myself."

"Now, just a minute," said Jim, still gripping the gentleman's sleeve, and drawing himself up. "I say I saw my friend drop it."

"Why," said the gentleman, pulling his arm free, "you two cheap thieves, trying to . . . Why, the very . . . I'll call a policeman at once, the very . . ."

"Call a cop," agreed Jim, loudly.

"No, no," I cried. "Jimmie, stop!"

The gentleman, pausing to stare grimly up and down, turned and walked proudly down the street.

"Why not let him call a cop? Let him call a cop," cried Jim.

"Don't be absurd," I pleaded. "Would a cop believe us against an obviously wealthy gentleman?"

"Gentleman," sneered Jim. "I never saw anybody so quick with his feet in my life. And I bet he was sixty."

"He's been stamping on dimes and nickels and quarters all his life, Jim," I said. "He's had practice."

"I've got a new idea for hell," said Jim, as we went slowly back to work, I jingled the twenty cents left in my pocket. "A special hell for rich men."

"Let's hear it," I said.

"It will be a vast chamber, immense," said Jim, raptly. "It will be entirely of black basalt or chalcedony. Jet black. It's floor will be polished and hard. Its walls will be filled with little cubby holes and niches in which the spirits of rich men will hide at night. But all day long, the Devil, sitting in a balcony up above and armed with a big scoop shovel, will keep shovelling scoopfuls of dimes and nickels out, and flinging them so that they will scatter all over that polished onyx floor, jingling and dancing and ringing and running and spinning. And there the spirits of the rich men, millions of them, bereft of all their earthly passions except their greatest one, will crawl and scramble and fight and claw like maniacs after the dimes and nickels. To all eternity, forever and ever, chasing madly, furiously, after the dimes and nickels."

"I'm glad you're just Jim Frise," I breathed.

"And they will all have little overalls on, with leather-lined pockets," said Jim. "And every night they take the dimes and nickels into the little caves in the vast walls of chalcedony or onyx. But every morning, when they wake, all the dimes and nickels will be gone."

"Oh, Jimmie," I protested. "That is the cruellest thing I ever heard of."

"Sure," said Jim. "But it's just a human little fancy. I'm human. Cops are human. Rich men are human. Everybody's human. So let me have my fancies, the same as everybody else."

So we went to the Morgue, as we call a newspaper filing room, and we hunted all through the clippings and pictures of the local rich men, but we couldn't find any trace, even in the Morgue, of the little man with the shut face who got my fifty cents.

So that made it possible for us to write this story. Because if we knew who he was, we probably wouldn't dare.

Antipathies

December 28, 1935

"What's it stuffed with?" asked the doctor, prying his finger under the fish.

"How's your cold?" asked Jimmie Frise. "It isn't a cold," I explained, "It's an antipathy."

"A what?"

"An antipathy," I elucidated. "It is halfway between hay fever and asthma. It is something around me my inner being hates. Maybe it is this new suit. Maybe it's a potted plant in my house. Maybe it's our pet dog, Dolly."

"What the heck are you talking about?" requested Jim.

"I've been to the doctor," I told him. "And he explained to me the latest stuff on asthma and hay fever and all those other sniffles. For ages, asthma was just

212

asthma, and old gentlemen and ladies just suffered and choked and finally died. But now they hold rabbit hunts."

"Hold what?" cried Jimmie, more and more indignant.

"Rabbit hunts, they call them," I assured Jim. "Two or three doctors will come to your house and hold a rabbit hunt. It is sort of like a detective story and a game of charades or hide the thimble. Two or three doctors, specialists, they will be, come to your house. And starting in the basement, they will go through your house like hunting for a needle in the haystack. They will examine every single item, big or small, in your home. It is worse than insurance adjusters. They start in the basement and study the asbestos insulation on your furnace. They inspect cocoanut matting, old rugs, plaster on walls."

"Pooh," said Jim.

"All right," I stated, "there is one case on record where the plasterer had used some kind of hair in the wall of the cellar. As the house grew old and the plaster broke, some of this hair was wafted up through the cracks in the floor, and caused an old gentleman untold agony. He thought he had asthma. What he had was a violent antipathy to that hair. Cow's hair, I think it was."

"Crazy," muttered Jim.

"Then these doctors will go through your living rooms," I went on. "They will see what pillows are stuffed with, and maybe it is feathers or rabbit fur or something. Maybe that is what is causing your asthma. They will examine rugs, tapestries, and even woodwork. They know of one case where a rich man was slowly suffocating with asthma every time he came into his house. They traced it down to one room, where he got the attacks worst. They eliminated everything, item by item, until they got to the cherrywood panelling of the living room. The fine, infinitesimal dust off that cherrywood was slowly killing the old man."

"I see," said Jim. "You are just trying to give me the jitters again."

"Listen," I declared. "You should seek knowledge. The more we know of science, the happier we will be."

"The more I hear of modern science," retorted Jim, "the more perilous life becomes. I would rather pine away and die of asthma, like hundreds of my forebears, just plain asthma, than to live in terror of dust off cherrywood panelling, or dandruff off a dog."

"These doctors," I started on.

"These detectives," scoffed Jim, "these rabbit hunters."

"These doctors," I insisted, "then study the pictures, the curtains, the rugs from China and India. You have no idea what funny furs and hairs the Chinese and Hindus use in their wools. Upstairs they examine the bed pillows, the mattresses, the upholstery. They look for potted plants, primroses and begonias. They see if they are discharging pollen or if they have fur on their leaves."

"Huh, huh," laughed Jimmie, hollowly.

"They look for pet birds, cats," I said. "Thousands of cats, silky dogs and canaries have been banished from homes because of the suffering they were inflicting."

"About the only place we are safe," muttered Jim, "is in a coffin."

"We know of any number of cases," I said, scientifically "where young ladies pinned a corsage bouquet of certain flowers on their gown, just before going to a dance, and they couldn't go because the were suddenly seized with a violent cold in the head. Stuffed up, eyes running and red, coughing, sneezing."

"Expectorating," suggested Jim. "Make it a swell picture. Be modern. Make it like those nice ads we read every day about this and that bad smell."

"Jim," I protested, "you can be old-fashioned, if you like. But I think you should be interested in the newer facts of medical science."

"Medical science," said Jim, "ought to know that what you don't know won't hurt you. I like the old-fashioned doctor who used to come in, set down his bag, blow his nose, rub his hands, and say well, well, well. I can't see these modern doctors coming in and staging a rabbit hunt in a man's home. The old doctor used to listen to your wheezes through a stethoscope. Then he would suddenly look wise. And write out a prescription for some brown medicine. And in a few days you were better."

"Or else you got worse and died," I sneered.

"Well, we all die anyway," Jim said. "And I would a darn sight sooner have it said of me that I died of asthma than that I died of goose-down."

"Suppose," I said, "you had a padded dressing gown, one of those comforter type of quilted dressing gowns. Suppose, you were slowly dying of asthma. Suppose the doctor said that the quilting in that dressing gown was the source of your trouble. What would you do?"

"If it was a dressing gown," said Jim, "that I loved, a dressing gown I had worn for fifteen years, and loved its every fold and rip and wrinkle, if it had held me snug through winters and autumns, wrapped me warm in bright mornings and hugged me tight to bed a thousand and one nights, been with me in my joys and sorrows, walked with me in the garden in June, comforted me when I was sick, if you are referring to my old dressing gown, then I assure you, sir, I would tell the doctor he was cracked, I would fold me up in that old dressing gown and go to my bed and lie there to the end. And I would direct that I be buried in that old dressing gown."

"I fear, Jim," I said, "you are just the average person. Well, I am not. I am vitally interested in the newer aspects of medical science. The doctors are coming to my house to-night to stage a rabbit hunt. There will be one old doctor and two young ones. Laboratory men. They are going to find the source of my trouble. Maybe it is our dog, Dolly. Maybe it is my bed pillow or an angora rug I have across the foot of my bed. Maybe it is the wall paper. I have a kind of fuzzy wallpaper in my den."

"Possibly you only need a haircut," offered Jim.

"Maybe," I went on, "it is the tobacco or cigarettes I use. They asked me what was new in my house. Well, I have a new suit."

"Harris tweed," observed Jim, narrowly. "Possibly it is some Scotch burrs in your schnozzle."

"I have a new buck's head mounted in my den," I went on. "They think it might be deer hair that is causing my complaint."

"May I attend the rabbit hunt?" asked Jim. "I would be most interested to watch the proceedings."

"Certainly," I agreed. "Come before eight. They'll be there at eight."

Jim was comfortably sunk in one of my den chairs, pipe smouldering, when the doctors arrived. The old doctor and two tall, grave young men. They set off their coats and hats, stacked their bags in the hall and, looking handsome and serious, proceeded to observe my house. They lifted cushions off chesterfields and probed for dust and only got hairpins. They turned oil paintings around and scraped samples of fuzz off the canvas at the back. They took, with fine scalpels, samples of the surface off wallpaper. Rugs, cushions, doilies or whatever they call them now, were pinched, shaken, sniffed and inspected under bright lights.

In the dining room, they went into committee on a vase full of artificial flowers.

"No pollen there," I laughed.

"No, but there is velvet," said the doctor. "And old velvet at that. This nap might be shedding. You can't tell what it might be."

Then they proceeded to the kitchen, the pantry, the cellar. They narrowly examined a row of pepper casters containing pepper, paprika, celery salt and onion salt, all my favorites.

In the den, they became obviously excited. They were like hounds coming hot to a scent.

They rubbed the buck's head and the moose head, and caught unseen particles in little paper envelopes. They took scrapings of my Navajo rugs and Mexican hairless blankets. With a small wisp of cotton, one of the young doctors stood up on chairs and collected dust from my old Hudson's Bay musket, my Queen Anne blunderbuss, my genuine Richard the Lion Heart crossbow that came from the Holy Land and was the one with which Blondel shot the message into Richard's high dungeon window. Of course it had dust. That goes for crossbows and the pennon from the lance of my old general's orderly or the shillelagh my great-grandfather swung all the way from Cork to York, Ontario.

But the doctors loved it. They grew flushed with joy.

"We think we will find the source of your trouble in here," stated the senior doctor. "What is this rag, here?"

"That, sir," I snorted, "is a fragment of the regimental flag of the 76th Hanoverian regiment which captured Gibraltar for the King of England and which I had the pleasure of fighting at Passchendaele."

"Get rid of it," said the doctor, picking it from the wall and dropping it distastefully on to the floor.

Surrounded by Dangers

"That fish," said the doctor, all three of them at point, like setters, staring at the five-pound, nine and five-eighths-ounce speckled trout I got in the Nipigon. "What is it stuffed with?"

"An Ojibway," I stated, "of my very dear acquaintance, did me the honor of stuffing that fish for me."

"What's it stuffed with?" repeated the doctor, reaching up, removing the birch bark plaque from the wall and prying his finger under the edge of the fish.

"Wait, wait," I cried.

"Get rid of it," said the doctor.

"Huh, huh, huh," laughed Jim, deep in his chair.

They came to my book shelves. My collection of piscatoria Americana et Canadiana brings men from Baltimore, St. Louis, even Seattle, just to see it. Millionaires have come all the way from Madison, Wis. just to touch some of my old books.

"This old junk," said the doctor. "Where did it come from? Who had it before? What's in some of that binding?"

He started to tear down some of the volumes from their shelves. I seized his arm.

"My dear sir," I gasped. "Nobody ever touches those books. Nobody. I don't keep them under glass simply because I think old books would die if they were imprisoned. But, sir, even I do not touch them."

"Get rid of them," said the doctor. "Simply full of dust, lint, hair, fur, felt and filth of every kind."

Jim got up out of his chair and stood looking out a window.

My botanical collection, made, I admit, thirty years ago, when I was young and ardent, is enclosed in two very large albums. The specimens are glued to the sheets and covered with a sort of cellophane. This the doctor tossed open, on its private table where I keep it. He and the two young men chuckled.

"Why," they laughed, "this alone would poison a

218

Antipathies

hundred men. Rotten with pollen; why, look, you even
have ragweed here. Enough to kill a hundred men for a
hundred years."

Dolly waddled in at this moment. Dolly with her black
and white silky fur, her long ears that sweep the floor,
her sad, gloomy spaniel eyes.

"How long have you had this dog?" asked the doctors.

"All its life," I said, as what else can one say of a dog?

"Get rid of it, it's the silky kind. Its hair fills this
house."

Jimmie turned from the window.

"Gentlemen," he said, "don't forget his fly fishing
gear. His fly books and boxes. His hundreds and
hundreds, yes, his thousands of trout flies; his fly tying
outfit, with packages of feathers from all over the world,
every kind of feather ever heard of."

The doctors looked at me. And I looked at Jim. It must
be the feeling a deer has, when the hounds close in.

"This," explained Jim, "is the season of the year he
ties flies and spends half the night staring at his fly
boxes. Get him to show them to you."

I had to. After all, science must be served.

The doctors looked at my two big tin pails with air-
tight lids in which I keep my flies and accessories from
the moths. They stared with amazement. They stared at
me. There was, I imagined, a faint light of the psychia-
trist in all their eyes.

"Get rid of all this," commanded the senior physician.
"There is enough irritating protein fibre in this one pail
to lay out a city of a hundred thousand souls. My dear
sir, some of these feathers come from India, China."

"The Malay archipelago," I added proudly, "New Zealand and Zanzibar."

"Get rid of it," said the doctor warmly. "And of course,
you have no right, in consideration of your antipathy, to
engage in any such trifling amusement as fly-tying. Take
up golf, sir. Golf is a gentleman's game."

We went downstairs. We sat in the living room, while
the doctors assembled and annotated all their little envelopes, and made notes.

Dolly waddled in, a bone sticking comically out of her

219

mouth like a cigar. One of her cutest tricks.

"What sort of a bone is that?" asked one of the younger research men, the one that looked a little Sherlock Holmesey.

"Pork chop," I replied.

All three physicians leaped to their feet.

"Pork chop," they cried.

"Pork chop," I confessed.

"How often do you eat pork chops?" hissed the older doctor.

"As often as God appoints," I said.

"Once a week?"

"About that."

"Did you have one before you came to see me yesterday?"

"I had two for breakfast," I stated calmly. "Yesterday morning."

"For breakfast?" gasped all three, incredulously.

"It is what we call a walking breakfast," I explained. "I get up and walk an hour before breakfast and come in to two chops or a steak. Maybe three boiled eggs. It keeps me in shape between the fishing and hunting seasons."

The doctors looked weakly at each other.

"Pork chops," said the senior physician, "are obviously your antipathy. That is the allergy. I have no doubt of it. You must give up pork chops. Certain proteins are the cause of your asthma. I feel perfectly confident it is the barbarous habit of eating pork chops for breakfast."

"Barbarous," agreed the two younger specialists.

I helped them into their coats. Jim helped too. We handed them all their bags. We stood even out on the cold porch to see them off. I eased the door shut.

"Huh, huh, huh," laughed Jim.

"I won't," I stated, "ever give up pork chops."

"For breakfast?" asked Jim.

"I'm going to have two," I sniffled, "tonight, as a bedtime snack."